# Safe use of work equipment

Provision and Use of Work Equipment Regulations 1998

Approved Code of Practice and guidance

**HSE Books**

**Approved Code of Practice**

This Code has been approved by the Health and Safety Executive, with the consent of the Secretary of State. It gives practical advice on how to comply with the law. If you follow the advice you will be doing enough to comply with the law in respect of those specific matters on which the Code gives advice. You may use alternative methods to those set out in the Code in order to comply with the law.

However, the Code has a special legal status. If you are prosecuted for breach of health and safety law, and it is proved that you did not follow the relevant provisions of the Code, you will need to show that you have complied with the law in some other way or a Court will find you at fault.

**Guidance**

This guidance is issued by the Health and Safety Executive. Following the guidance is not compulsory, unless specifically stated, and you are free to take other action. But if you do follow the guidance you will normally be doing enough to comply with the law. Health and safety inspectors seek to secure compliance with the law and may refer to this guidance.

# Contents

# Introduction

## About this book

1    This publication sets out what you should do to comply with the Provision and Use of Work Equipment Regulations 1998 (PUWER). The Approved Code of Practice (ACOP) text and associated guidance provide practical advice on how you can comply with the requirements of the Regulations.

## Who should read this book?

2    Employers, dutyholders and anyone else who has responsibility and/or control – directly or indirectly – for work equipment, such as managers and supervisors. Throughout this book we have referred to the employer and self-employed people who have duties as 'you'. Where the guidance is addressed to some other dutyholder, for example a competent person, the text makes it clear who it is intended for.

## What does PUWER apply to?

3    PUWER applies to the provision and use of all work equipment. It cannot be considered in isolation from other health and safety legislation. In particular, it needs to be considered with the requirements of the Health and Safety at Work etc Act 1974 ('the HSW Act').[1] The ACOP material and guidance contained in this publication will highlight where this is the case.

4    There is also some overlap between PUWER and other sets of regulations, for example:

(a)    The Lifting Operations and Lifting Equipment Regulations 1998[2] (LOLER) apply over and above the general requirements of PUWER in dealing with specific hazards/risks associated with lifting equipment and lifting operations;

(b)    The Workplace (Health, Safety and Welfare) Regulations 1992 ('the Workplace Regulations')[3] which cover workplace risks to pedestrians from vehicles;

(c)    The Health and Safety (Display Screen Equipment) Regulations 1992,[4] for example, on lighting;

(d)    The Personal Protective Equipment at Work Regulations 1992 ('the PPE Regulations'),[5] for example, on maintenance;

(e)    The Construction (Design and Management) Regulations 2007 ('CDM');[6]

(f)    The Road Vehicles (Construction and Use) Regulations 1986;[7]

(g)    The Work at Height Regulations 2005 ('the Work at Height Regulations') (relating to inspection of work equipment for use when working at height);[8]

(h)    The Management of Health and Safety at Work Regulations 1999 ('the Management Regulations') relating to risk assessments.[9]

5    If you comply with the more specific regulations, it will normally be enough to comply with the more general requirements in PUWER.

6    There are two related PUWER ACOPs which deal in greater detail with the safe use of power presses, L112[10] and the safe use of woodworking machinery L114.[11]

## Where does PUWER apply?

7    PUWER applies to all workplaces and work situations where the HSW Act applies and extends beyond the mainland of Great Britain to specified offshore areas and activities.

## What are the differences between this book and the previous edition?

8    The changes, which are summarised below, have been widely consulted on.

9    Changes in this edition include:

(a)    the introduction of short summaries before regulations to help the reader and direct them to other relevant information;
(b)    removal of much of the old introduction and background information;
(c)    references to PUWER 98 have been replaced simply by PUWER;
(d)    minor amendments to ACOP paragraphs, where necessary, to update information;
(e)    guidance material has been simplified where possible and more use made of lists.

## About ACOPs

10    Approved Codes of Practice are approved by the HSE Board with the consent of the Secretary of State. See 'Appendix 3: Notice of Approval' for details.

11    ACOP text explains how to comply with the law in a specific way and has a special status in law. If you do not follow the advice in ACOP text and you are prosecuted for a breach of the law, the court will take your breach of the law as proven unless you can show that you have complied with the law in another equally effective way. If you follow the advice in an ACOP, you can be sure that you will be doing enough to comply with the law.

12    Guidance text is different – following it is not compulsory, unless specifically stated. If you follow it, you will normally be doing enough to comply with the law, but you may use other methods. The ACOP describes preferred or recommended methods that can be used (or standards to be met) to comply with the Regulations and the duties imposed by the HSW Act. The accompanying guidance also provides advice on achieving compliance, or it may give information of a general nature, including explanation of the requirements of the law, more specific technical information or references to further sources of information.

13    The legal status of ACOP and guidance text is given on the copyright page.

## Presentation

14    The ACOP text is set out in **bold** and the accompanying guidance in normal type, the text of the regulations is in *italics*. Coloured borders also indicate each section clearly. Some regulations are preceded by a short summary of the main

duties imposed by that regulation. This text has no 'status' (such as ACOP/guidance) and is for information only. Its purpose is to help the reader navigate the document.

# The Regulations

## Regulation 1 Citation and commencement

| Regulation | 1 |
|---|---|

*These Regulations may be cited as the Provision and Use of Work Equipment Regulations 1998 and shall come into force on 5th December 1998.*

## Regulation 2 Interpretation

| Regulation | 2 |
|---|---|

*(1)   In these Regulations, unless the context otherwise requires—*

*"the 1974 Act" means the Health and Safety at Work etc. Act 1974;*

*"employer" except in regulation 3(2) and (3) includes a person to whom the requirements imposed by these Regulations apply by virtue of regulation 3(3)(a) and (b);*

*"essential requirements" means requirements described in regulation 10(1);*

*"the Executive" means the Health and Safety Executive;*

*"inspection" in relation to an inspection under paragraph (1) or (2) of regulation 6—*

*(a)   means such visual or more rigorous inspection by a competent person as is appropriate for the purpose described in the paragraph;*
*(b)   where it is appropriate to carry out testing for the purpose, includes testing the nature and extent of which are appropriate for the purpose;*

*"power press" means a press or press brake for the working of metal by means of tools, or for die proving, which is power driven and which embodies a flywheel and clutch;*

*"thorough examination" in relation to a thorough examination under paragraph (1), (2), (3) or (4) of regulation 32—*

*(a)   means a thorough examination by a competent person;*
*(b)   includes testing the nature and extent of which are appropriate for the purpose described in the paragraph;*

*"use" in relation to work equipment means any activity involving work equipment and includes starting, stopping, programming, setting, transporting, repairing, modifying, maintaining, servicing and cleaning;*

*"work equipment" means any machinery, appliance, apparatus, tool or installation for use at work (whether exclusively or not);*

*and related expressions shall be construed accordingly.*

**Regulation**    **2**

*(2)    Any reference in regulations 32 to 34 or Schedule 3 to a guard or protection device is a reference to a guard or protection device provided for the tools of a power press.*

*(3)    Any reference in regulation 32 or 33 to a guard or protection device being on a power press shall, in the case of a guard or protection device designed to operate while adjacent to a power press, be construed as a reference to its being adjacent to it.*

*(4)    Any reference in these Regulations to—*

*(a)    a numbered regulation or Schedule is a reference to the regulation or Schedule in these Regulations so numbered; and*

*(b)    a numbered paragraph is a reference to the paragraph so numbered in the regulation in which the reference appears.*

**Guidance**    **2**

## Inspection

15    The term 'inspection' is used in PUWER. The purpose of an inspection is to identify whether the equipment can be operated, adjusted and maintained safely and that any deterioration (for example, any defect, damage or wear) can be detected and remedied before it results in unacceptable risks.

## Use

16    The definition of 'use' is wide and includes all activities involving work equipment such as stopping or starting the equipment, repair, modification, maintenance and servicing. In addition to operations normally considered as use, cleaning and transport of the equipment are also included. In this context 'transport' means, for example using a lift truck to carry goods around a warehouse.

## Work equipment

17    The scope of 'work equipment' is extremely wide. It covers almost any equipment used at work, including:

(a)    'toolbox tools' such as hammers, knives, handsaws, meat cleavers etc;
(b)    single machines such as drilling machines, circular saws, photocopiers, combine harvesters, dumper trucks etc;
(c)    apparatus such as laboratory apparatus (Bunsen burners etc);
(d)    lifting equipment such as hoists, lift trucks, elevating work platforms, lifting slings etc;
(e)    other equipment such as ladders, pressure water cleaners etc;
(f)    an installation such as a series of machines connected together, for example a paper-making line or enclosure for providing sound insulation or scaffolding or similar access equipment (except where CDM imposes more detailed requirements).

18    PUWER applies to work equipment (as identified in regulation 2) whether it is new, existing or second-hand.

19    'Installation' does not include an offshore installation, but it does include any equipment attached or connected to it.

20    The following are not classified as work equipment:

(a)    livestock;
(b)    substances (for example acids, alkalis, slurry, cement, water);
(c)    structural items (for example walls, stairs, roofs, fences);
(d)    private cars.

## Motor vehicles

21    Motor vehicles being used for work activities, which are not privately owned fall within the scope of PUWER. When these vehicles are used on public roads or in a public place, the more specific road traffic legislation takes precedence. When such vehicles are used off the public highway and the road traffic law does not apply, for example on a dock road, PUWER and the HSW Act would normally take precedence unless relevant local by-laws are in operation – for example, road traffic by-laws at some airports. Drivers should hold a Department for Transport driving licence and vehicles should be maintained to the normal standards required for use on the public highway, ie they should have an MOT certificate, where necessary, or be maintained to equivalent standards where statutory testing is not a legal requirement.

## Aircraft

22    The design, operation and maintenance of civilian aircraft airworthiness is subject to other specific legislation, such as the Air Navigation Order 2009.[12] This legislation takes precedence over PUWER.

## When is an employee considered to be 'at work'?

23    Section 52(1)(b) and (c) of the HSW Act says that 'an employee is at work throughout the time when he is in the course of his employment, but not otherwise', and 'a self-employed person is at work throughout such time as he devotes to work as a self-employed person.'

# Regulation 3 Application

(1)    These Regulations shall apply—

(a)    in Great Britain; and
(b)    outside Great Britain as sections 1 to 59 and 80 to 82 of the 1974 Act apply by virtue of the Health and Safety at Work etc. Act 1974 (Application outside Great Britain) Order 1995 ("the 1995 Order").

(2)    The requirements imposed by these Regulations on an employer in respect of work equipment shall apply to such equipment provided for use or used by an employee of his at work.

(3)    The requirements imposed by these Regulations on an employer shall also apply—

(a)    to a self-employed person, in respect of work equipment he uses at work;
(b)    subject to paragraph (5), to a person who has control to any extent of—
(i)    work equipment;

**Regulation 3**

(ii)   a person at work who uses or supervises or manages the use of work equipment; or

(iii)   the way in which work equipment is used at work,

and to the extent of his control.

(4)   Any reference in paragraph (3)(b) to a person having control is a reference to a person having control in connection with the carrying on by him of a trade, business or other undertaking (whether for profit or not).

(5)   The requirements imposed by these Regulations shall not apply to a person in respect of work equipment supplied by him by way of sale, agreement for sale or hire-purchase agreement.

(6)   Subject to paragraphs (7) to (10), these Regulations shall not impose any obligation in relation to a ship's work equipment (whether that equipment is used on or off the ship).

(7)   Where merchant shipping requirements are applicable to a ship's work equipment, paragraph (6) shall relieve the shore employer of his obligations under these Regulations in respect of that equipment only where he has taken all reasonable steps to satisfy himself that the merchant shipping requirements are being complied with in respect of that equipment.

(8)   In a case where the merchant shipping requirements are not applicable to the ship's work equipment by reason only that for the time being there is no master, crew or watchman on the ship, those requirements shall nevertheless be treated for the purpose of paragraph (7) as if they were applicable.

(9)   Where the ship's work equipment is used in a specified operation paragraph (6) shall not apply to regulations 7 to 9, 11 to 13, 20 to 22 and 30 (each as applied by regulation 3).

(10)   Paragraph (6) does not apply to a ship's work equipment provided for use or used in an activity (whether carried on in or outside Great Britain) specified in the 1995 Order save that it does apply to—

(a)   the loading, unloading, fuelling or provisioning of the ship; or

(b)   the construction, reconstruction, finishing, refitting, repair, maintenance, cleaning or breaking up of the ship.

(11)   In this regulation—

"master" has the meaning assigned to it by section 313(1) of the Merchant Shipping Act 1995;

"merchant shipping requirements" means the requirements of regulations 3 and 4 of the Merchant Shipping (Guarding of Machinery and Safety of Electrical Equipment) Regulations 1988 and regulations 5 to 10 of the Merchant Shipping (Hatches and Lifting Plant) Regulations 1988;

"ship" has the meaning assigned to it by section 313(1) of the Merchant Shipping Act 1995 save that it does not include an offshore installation;

"shore employer" means an employer of persons (other than the master and crew of any ship) who are engaged in a specified operation;

**Regulation**     **3**

*"specified operation" means an operation in which the ship's work equipment is used—*

*(a)    by persons other than the master and crew; or*
*(b)    where persons other than the master and crew are liable to be exposed to a risk to their health or safety from its use.*

**Guidance**     **3**

## Where PUWER applies

24    PUWER applies:

(a)    to all sectors where the HSW Act applies, not only factories, offices and shops but also, for example schools, universities, hospitals, hotels, places of entertainment and offshore oil and gas installations;

(b)    to work equipment used in the common parts of shared buildings (such as lifts), private roads and paths on industrial estates and business parks and temporary work sites, including construction sites;

(c)    throughout Great Britain and has effect wherever work is done by the employed or the self-employed except for domestic work in a private household;

(d)    to equipment used by homeworkers; and to hotels, nursing homes and similar establishments and to parts of workplaces where 'domestic' staff are employed, such as the kitchens of hostels or sheltered accommodation.

## Who has duties under PUWER?

25    PUWER places duties on:

(a)    employers;
(b)    the self-employed;
(c)    people who have control of work equipment.

The duty on people who have control of work equipment reflects the way that work equipment is used in industry where there may not necessarily be a direct 'employment' relationship between the user and the person who controls the work equipment. For example, temporary workers supplied by an employment business ('agency') will be under the control of a user business (often called the client or hirer) that uses their services, and which will have duties towards them under regulation 3(3)(b). Similarly, where a subcontractor carries out work at another person's premises with work equipment provided by that person or someone else who controls the equipment but not its use, such as a plant hire company. This approach is in line with that taken in CDM, LOLER and in the Work at Height Regulations.

26    Although only the courts can give an authoritative interpretation of the law, in considering the application of these Regulations and ACOP/guidance to people working under another's direction, the following information should be considered: if people working under the control and direction of others are treated as self-employed for tax and national insurance purposes, they are nevertheless treated as their employees for health and safety purposes. It may therefore be necessary to take appropriate action to protect them. If any doubt exists about who is responsible for the health and safety of a worker this should be clarified and included in the terms of the contract. However, a legal duty under the HSW Act cannot be passed on by means of a contract and there will still be duties towards

**Guidance**    **3**

others under section 3 of the HSW Act. If such workers are employed on the basis that they are responsible for their own health and safety, legal advice should be sought before doing so.

## Employer's duties

27   If you are an employer (whether as an individual, partnership or company) you have a duty to ensure that items of work equipment provided for your employees and the self-employed working for you comply with PUWER. You have a legal duty to consult with your employees on matters relating to health and safety in the workplace. For further information see the HSE leaflet *Consulting employees on health and safety: A brief guide to the law*[13] or see HSE's worker involvement web pages at www.hse.gov.uk/involvement.

## Self-employed people's duties

28   If you are self-employed, you have a duty to ensure that work equipment you provide for work or use at work complies with PUWER.

## The duties of 'those in control of work equipment'

29   If you provide work equipment for use at work, where you do not control its use or the premises where it is to be used, you should still ensure that the work equipment complies with PUWER. People in control of non-domestic premises who provide work equipment which is used by other people at work should also comply with PUWER. PUWER places duties on employers and the self-employed; offshore this includes owners, operators and contractors. Their duties cover both their own employees and, as people having control of work equipment, other workers who may be affected. Meeting these duties where a number of employers and their employees are involved requires co-operation and co-ordination of activities. For example, the owner of a multi-occupied building has a legal responsibility to ensure that a lift complies with the Regulations, and the main contractor of a construction site would be responsible for a scaffold.

## Employees' duties

30   If you are an employee you do not have any specific duties under PUWER, but you do have general legal duties to take reasonable care of yourself and others who could be affected by your actions, and to co-operate with your employer so that your employer can comply with their health and safety duties and requirements. If you are an employee, or working under someone else's control, the law says you must:

(a)   report any safety hazard you identify to your employer;

(b)   use the equipment and safety devices supplied or given to you properly, in accordance with any training and instructions (unless you think that would be unsafe, in which case you should seek further instructions before continuing).

**Guidance** 3

## Where employees provide their own work equipment for use at work

31    PUWER also covers situations where employees provide their own work equipment. For example, where builders use their own trowels or hammers.

## Multi-occupancy or multi-occupier sites

32    On multi-occupancy or multi-contractor sites where several dutyholders share the use of equipment, you must agree among yourselves that one of you takes responsibility for ensuring that the equipment complies with PUWER (and any other relevant legislation), particularly regulation 11 of the Management Regulations. Paragraphs 33–39 examine such situations in detail in the construction and offshore sectors, but similar principles apply in other sectors.

## Application to the construction industry

33    In the construction industry items of work equipment on sites are often used by a number of different contractors. Regulation 3 places a duty on each contractor to ensure that any work equipment used by their employees (or themselves in the case of self-employed contractors) conforms to, and is used in accordance with, these Regulations.

34    It also requires, to the extent that their control allows, the same duty from those people who exercise control over the equipment or the way that it is used. For example, people hiring out equipment for others to use often play the leading role in inspecting and maintaining the equipment since they determine the maintenance schedules and availability of their machines. On the other hand, the users may be more directly concerned, for example, with organising, instructing and training their employees to use it safely since the conduct of their own employees is a matter for them rather than the hirer.

35    The actions of others, such as hirers, may help employers and the self-employed to meet their duties. However, that does not reduce the employer's or the self-employed person's duty to make sure that they are meeting the requirements of the Regulations. Effective co-ordination between everyone involved is essential to make sure that everyone meets their legal duties.

36    The arrangements required by regulation 11 of the Management Regulations have been strengthened by CDM.

37    CDM requires the appointment of a single person or firm ('the principal contractor') to co-ordinate health and safety matters on site. The principal contractor also has a duty to ensure that all contractors co-operate on health and safety matters. Where the use of equipment by a wide range of people from a number of different employers requires particular attention or co-ordination, this should be addressed in the construction phase health and safety plan. Co-operation and exchanging information is vital when equipment is shared. All users need to know:

(a)    who is responsible for the co-ordination of the equipment;
(b)    that changes in conditions of use need to be reported to that person;
(c)    whether there are any limitations on the use of the equipment;
(d)    how the equipment can be used safely.

| Guidance | 3 |
|---|---|

## Application to the offshore industry

38    PUWER applies offshore as the HSW Act applies by virtue of the Health and Safety at Work etc Act 1974 (Application outside Great Britain) Order 2013.[14] This Order applies the HSW Act to offshore installations, wells, pipelines and pipeline works, and to connected activities within the territorial waters of Great Britain or in designated areas of the United Kingdom Continental Shelf, plus certain other activities within territorial waters.

39    PUWER places duties on employers and the self-employed; offshore this includes owners, operators and contractors. Their duties cover both their own employees and, as people having control of work equipment, other workers who may be affected. Meeting these duties where a number of employers and their employees are involved requires co-operation and co-ordination of activities. The person in control of an operation should ensure that adequate arrangements are in place to ensure that work equipment provided for use at work is suitable, properly used and maintained etc. This will often be an installation owner or operator, for example, but contractors who take equipment offshore are primarily responsible for risks arising from that equipment.

## How does PUWER apply to marine activities?

40    The principals of PUWER apply to ships as laid down in The Merchant Shipping and Fishing Vessels (PUWER) Regulations 2006.[15] The Maritime and Coastguard Agency (MCA) (see www.gov.uk/government/organisations/maritime-and-coastguard-agency) regulates ships under the Merchant Shipping legislation, this includes Government Ships (as defined under section 308 of the Merchant Shipping Act 1995)[16] that have been registered under part ii of that Act by order in council, but excludes all other ships belonging to HM Navy. Regulations 7–9, 11–13, 20–22 and 30 of PUWER will apply in what are called 'specified operations'. Specified operations are where the ships' equipment is used by people other than the master and crew of the vessel or where only the master and crew are involved in the work, but other people are put at risk by the work being carried out. There is a Memorandum of Understanding (MOU) (at www.hse.gov.uk/aboutus/howwework/framework/mou/mcamou.pdf) between the Health and Safety Executive, the Maritime and Coastguard Agency and the Marine Accident Investigation Branch (see www.gov.uk/government/organisations/maritime-accident-investigation-branch) for health and safety activities etc at the water margin and offshore.

41    Where shore-based workers are to use ship's equipment, and their employers wish to take advantage of this disapplication from PUWER, they are required to take reasonable steps to satisfy themselves that the appropriate merchant shipping requirements have been met. The ship's records should normally contain enough information to satisfy reasonable enquiries.

42    PUWER may apply to other work equipment not belonging to, but used on board a ship, for example where a shore-based contractor carries out work on a ship within territorial waters. Work equipment used in such circumstances would be subject to PUWER but PUWER does not apply to foreign registered vessels on passage.

43    Most mobile offshore installations are also ships. PUWER applies to mobile installations while at or near their working stations and when in transit to their working stations. It also applies to work equipment used on ships for the purposes of carrying out activities in connection with offshore installations or wells and for pipeline works.

**Guidance** 3

44 Legal requirements for co-operation between offshore dutyholders are set out in the Offshore Installations (Safety Case) Regulations 2005[17] and the Offshore Installations and Pipeline Works (Management and Administration) Regulations 1995.[18]

45 Equipment for use on offshore installations that is safety-critical, as defined by regulation 2(1) of the Offshore Installations (Safety Case) Regulations 2005, will be subject to the verification arrangements required by those Regulations.

## Who does not have duties under PUWER?

46 If you provide work equipment as part of a work activity for use by members of the public, you do not have duties under PUWER. Examples are compressed air equipment on a garage forecourt or lifts provided for use by the public in a shopping centre. In cases such as this, members of the public will continue to be protected by the requirements of the HSW Act.

---

### Summary of regulation 4

This regulation deals with the safety of work equipment from three aspects:
- its initial integrity;
- the place where it will be used;
- the purpose for which it will be used.

There is no specific regulation requiring a risk assessment in PUWER. Instead the requirement to carry out a risk assessment is contained in the Management Regulations, which have general provisions relating to the safety of work equipment.

---

## Regulation 4 Suitability of work equipment

**Regulation** 4

*(1) Every employer shall ensure that work equipment is so constructed or adapted as to be suitable for the purpose for which it is used or provided.*

*(2) In selecting work equipment, every employer shall have regard to the working conditions and to the risks to the health and safety of persons which exist in the premises or undertaking in which that work equipment is to be used and any additional risk posed by the use of that work equipment.*

*(3) Every employer shall ensure that work equipment is used only for operations for which, and under conditions for which, it is suitable.*

*(4) In this regulation "suitable" —*

*(a) subject to sub-paragraph (b), means suitable in any respect which it is reasonably foreseeable will affect the health or safety of any person;*
*(b) in relation to—*
*(i) an offensive weapon within the meaning of section 1(4) of the Prevention of Crime Act 1953 provided for use as self-defence or as deterrent equipment; and*
*(ii) work equipment provided for use for arrest or restraint, by a person who holds the office of constable or an appointment as police cadet, means suitable in any respect which it is reasonably foreseeable will affect the health or safety of such person.\**

*Paragraph (4) substituted by SI 1999/860, regulation 5(1).

| Guidance | 4 |
|---|---|

## How risk assessment and the Management Regulations link with PUWER

47    Risks to health and safety should be assessed taking into account the type of work equipment, substances and electrical or mechanical hazards to which people may be exposed.

48    Action to eliminate/control any risk might include, for example, during maintenance:

(a)    disconnecting the power supply to the work equipment;
(b)    supporting parts of the work equipment which could fall;
(c)    securing mobile work equipment so it cannot move;
(d)    removing or isolating flammable or hazardous substances;
(e)    depressurising pressurised equipment.

49    Consider environmental conditions such as:

(a)    lighting;
(b)    problems caused by weather conditions;
(c)    other work being carried out which may affect the operation;
(d)    the activities of people who are not at work.

50    You have a duty under health and safety law to ensure, as far as reasonably practicable (see www.hse.gov.uk/risk/theory/alarpglance.htm), the health, safety and welfare of your employees and others such as temporary workers supplied through an employment agency.

51    When carrying out an assessment of the risk to their health and safety, you should identify groups of workers that might be particularly at risk, such as young or disabled people, or those whose first language is not English. The outcome of your risk assessment will help you to meet your duty to provide the information, instruction, training and supervision necessary to ensure the health and safety of your employees. You should take account of factors such as their competence, experience and maturity. Formal qualifications, training certificates, aptitude tests etc can be used to help you identify competence. You can find more guidance at www.hse.gov.uk/competence.

### Managing health and safety

52    A good management system can:

(a)    help you identify problem areas;
(b)    help you decide what actions you should take;
(c)    check that the action you have taken has been effective.

Guidance on managing health and safety can be found at www.hse.gov.uk/managing.

**Guidance** 4

## Regulation 4(1)

53    Equipment must be suitable, by design, construction or adaptation, for the actual work it is provided to do. This means that when you provide work equipment you have to make sure it is suitable for the work being done and is used in accordance with the manufacturer's specifications and instructions. If work equipment is adapted it must still be suitable for its intended purpose.

## Regulation 4(2)

54    You must assess the location where the work equipment is being used and take account of any risks that may arise from the particular circumstances. The risks involved may mean that you cannot use the work equipment in a particular place. For example, electrically powered equipment is not suitable for use in wet or flammable atmospheres unless it is designed for this purpose. In such circumstances you should consider selecting suitably protected electrical equipment or alternative pneumatically or hydraulically powered equipment.

55    The risk assessment carried out under regulation 3(1) of the Management Regulations will help you to select work equipment and assess its suitability for particular tasks. There is guidance available in *Risk assessment: A brief guide to controlling risks in the workplace.*[19] There are example risk assessments on the HSE website that show the approach HSE expects businesses to take. These examples are specifically aimed at small and medium-sized businesses but they may provide a useful starting point regardless of the size of the business involved (see www.hse.gov.uk/risk/casestudies/index.htm).

56    Most dutyholders will be able to assess the risks themselves using expertise from within their organisations to identify the measures to be taken regarding their work equipment. Where there are complex hazards or equipment, you may want to get help from external health and safety advisers, appointed under regulation 7 of the Management Regulations.

**ACOP** 4

## Ergonomics

**57    When selecting work equipment, employers should take account of ergonomic risks.**

**Guidance** 4

58    Ergonomics is a risk factor you should consider. Ergonomic design takes account of the size and shape of the human body and should ensure that the design is compatible with human dimensions. Operating positions, working heights, reach distances etc can be adapted to accommodate the intended operator. Operation of the equipment should not place undue strain on the user. Operators should not be expected to exert undue force or stretch or reach beyond their normal strength or physical reach limitations to carry out tasks. This is particularly important for highly repetitive work such as working on supermarket checkouts or high-speed 'pick and place' operations.

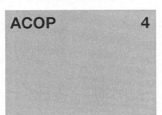

**ACOP** 4

**59    You should ensure that work equipment is installed, located and used in such a way as to reduce risks to users of work equipment and for other workers, such as ensuring that there is enough space between the moving parts of work equipment and fixed or moving parts in its environment.**

**60    When determining the suitability of work equipment, you should ensure that where appropriate:**

ACOP    4

(a)    all forms of energy used or produced; and
(b)    all substances used or produced;

can be supplied and/or removed safely.

**61    You should ensure that where mobile work equipment with a combustion engine is in use there is sufficient air of good quality.**

Guidance    4

62    Work equipment itself can sometimes cause risks to health and safety in particular locations which would otherwise be safe. An example is a petrol engine generator discharging exhaust fumes into an enclosed space.

## Why ventilation may be necessary

63    Exhaust gases from mobile work equipment with a combustion engine contributes significantly to airborne pollution in workplaces. For example, in motor vehicle workshops, underground car parks, in buildings where lift trucks are used and in tunnels. In such circumstances, a high standard of ventilation and/or extraction is needed to dilute toxic combustion products (such as carbon monoxide, carbon dioxide and oxides of nitrogen) to an acceptable level. Combustion products can be harmful to health if there is not enough fresh air for people to breathe.

## When to ventilate workplaces

64    Ventilation requirements vary depending on the type of fuel, condition of the engine and pattern of use. If mobile work equipment is fitted with pollution control services, lower ventilation rates may be necessary. The method of ventilation depends on where the work equipment is used, for example in a warehouse or a tunnel and if there is not enough good quality air naturally available, it should be supplied.

## How to ensure there is enough clean air

65    Examples of how to ensure there is enough clean air include:

(a)    the exhausts of stationary vehicles under test or repair should be connected to exhaust removal systems;
(b)    flexible exhaust systems or box filters should be used where necessary;
(c)    natural and/or mechanical ventilation should be used where necessary;
(d)    air quality should be monitored regularly to ensure that the control systems in place are working properly.

## Ventilation requirements of the Workplace Regulations

66    Regulation 6 of the Workplace Regulations[3] contains general requirements about ventilation of the workplace and equipment used to ventilate workplaces.

## The Confined Spaces Regulations 1997

67    The Confined Spaces Regulations 1997 do not allow the use of petrol-fuelled internal combustion engines in a confined space unless special precautions are

**Guidance** 4

taken. Other forms of fuel such as diesel or gas are nearly as dangerous and are not appropriate unless adequate precautions are taken. Where their use is unavoidable, adequate ventilation needs to be provided to prevent a build-up of harmful gases. Full guidance on the Confined Spaces Regulations 1997 is contained in HSE's publication *Confined spaces. A brief guide to working safely*.[20]

### Control of Substances Hazardous to Health Regulations 2002 (COSHH)

68    Under regulation 7 of COSHH[21] employers must prevent or control the exposure of employees to substances hazardous to health.

### Regulation 4(3)

69    Work equipment must be used only for tasks that it is fit for and in conditions for which it is suitable, for example:

(a)    a circular saw is generally not suitable for cutting a rebate, whereas a spindle moulding machine would be suitable, because it can be guarded to a high standard;

(b)    knives with unprotected blades are often used for cutting operations where scissors or other cutting tools could be used, which would reduce both the probability and severity of injury.

---

**Summary of regulation 5**

This regulation builds on the general duty in the HSW Act which requires work equipment to be maintained so that it is safe.

It does not cover the maintenance process (that is covered by the general duties of the HSW Act) or the construction of work equipment, so that maintenance can be carried out without risk to health or safety (that is covered by regulations 10 and 22 of PUWER).

---

## Regulation 5 Maintenance

**Regulation** 5

*(1)    Every employer shall ensure that work equipment is maintained in an efficient state, in efficient working order and in good repair.*

*(2)    Every employer shall ensure that where any machinery has a maintenance log, the log is kept up to date.*

**Guidance** 5

70    Equipment must be maintained so that its performance does not deteriorate to the extent that people are put at risk. In regulation 5, 'efficient' relates to how the condition of the equipment might affect health and safety. It is not concerned with productivity. Some parts of equipment such as guards, ventilation equipment, emergency shutdown systems and pressure relief devices have to be maintained to do their job at all times. The need to maintain other parts may not be as obvious. For example, failure to lubricate bearings or replace clogged filters might lead to danger because of seized parts or overheating. Some maintenance routines affect both the way the equipment works and its safety. Checking and replacing worn or damaged friction linings in the clutch on a guillotine will ensure it operates correctly, but could also prevent the drive mechanism jamming, so reducing the risk of repeat unintentional strokes.

| Guidance | 5 |
| --- | --- |

## Frequency of maintenance

71    Equipment should be checked frequently to ensure that safety-related features are functioning correctly. A fault which affects production is normally apparent within a short time; however, a fault in a safety-critical system could remain undetected unless appropriate safety checks are included in maintenance activities.

72    The frequency of maintenance activities should take into account the:

(a)    intensity of use – frequency and maximum working limits;
(b)    operating environment, for example marine, outdoors;
(c)    variety of operations – is the equipment performing the same task all the time or does this change?
(d)    risk to health and safety from malfunction or failure.

## Maintenance management

73    The extent and complexity of maintenance can vary considerably from simple checks on basic equipment to integrated programmes for complex plant. In all circumstances, for maintenance to be effective, it should be targeted at the parts of work equipment where failure or deterioration could lead to health and safety risks. Maintenance should address those parts which have failed or are likely to deteriorate and lead to health and safety risks.

74    Simple hand tools usually require minimal maintenance, but could need repair or replacement at intervals. More complex powered equipment will normally be accompanied by a manufacturer's maintenance manual, which specifies routine and special maintenance procedures to be carried out at particular intervals. Maintenance procedures should be carried out in accordance with the manufacturer's recommendations which relate to the equipment, for example periodic lubrication, replacement and adjustment of parts.

75    Where safety-critical parts could fail and cause the equipment, guards or other protection devices to fail and lead to immediate or hidden potential risks, a formal system of planned preventative or condition-based maintenance is needed.

76    Additional maintenance measures may be required if particularly arduous conditions of use are foreseen or have been experienced in use. There may be times when these additional measures need to be reviewed and revised in the light of ongoing operating experiences.

77    If items of plant and equipment are hired, it is important for both the hire company and the person responsible for hiring the equipment to establish who will carry out safety-related maintenance. This is particularly important when equipment is on long-term hire. The terms of the agreement should be set out or recorded in writing. If the hire company is some distance from the user site, it might be uneconomical for their staff to carry out simple checks and make minor adjustments, so the user may agree to carry them out. However, both parties should agree exactly what they are responsible for and make sure that this is communicated to the people who will be carrying out the maintenance.

## Maintenance log

78    There is no requirement for you to keep a maintenance log. Although it is recommended that you keep a record of maintenance for high-risk equipment. A

**Guidance**      5

detailed maintenance log can provide information for future planning of maintenance activities and inform maintenance personnel what actions have been taken previously.

## Maintenance workers

79    Maintenance work should only be done by people who are competent to do the work. For details of the information, instructions and training required, see regulations 8–9.

---

**Summary of regulation 6**

Regulation 6 covers the extent and nature of the inspection. It deals with:
- the different situations where inspection of work equipment is required;
- the purpose of the inspection in each case;
- who should carry out the inspection;
- keeping records of inspections;
- the work equipment that is not covered by regulation 6, and why.

---

# Regulation 6 Inspection

**Regulation**      6

*(1)    Every employer shall ensure that, where the safety of work equipment depends on the installation conditions, it is inspected—*

*(a)    after installation and before being put into service for the first time; or*
*(b)    after assembly at a new site or in a new location,*

*to ensure that it has been installed correctly and is safe to operate.*

*(2)    Every employer shall ensure that work equipment exposed to conditions causing deterioration which is liable to result in dangerous situations is inspected—*

*(a)    at suitable intervals; and*
*(b)    each time that exceptional circumstances which are liable to jeopardise the safety of the work equipment have occurred,*

*to ensure that health and safety conditions are maintained and that any deterioration can be detected and remedied in good time.*

*(3)    Every employer shall ensure that the result of an inspection made under this regulation is recorded and kept until the next inspection under this regulation is recorded.*

*(4)    Every employer shall ensure that no work equipment—*

*(a)    leaves his undertaking; or*
*(b)    if obtained from the undertaking of another person, is used in his undertaking,*

*unless it is accompanied by physical evidence that the last inspection required to be carried out under this regulation has been carried out.*

*(5)    This regulation does not apply to—*

*(a)    a power press to which regulations 32 to 35 apply;*

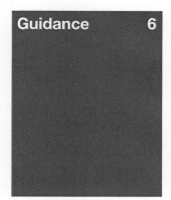

**Regulation**     6

*(b)*   *a guard or protection device for the tools of such power press;*
*(c)*   *work equipment for lifting loads including persons;*
*(d)*   *winding apparatus to which the Mines (Shafts and Winding) Regulations 1993 apply;*
*(e)*   *work equipment required to be inspected by regulations 31(4) or 32(2) of the Construction (Design and Management) Regulations 2007;\**
*(f)*   *work equipment to which regulation 12 of the Work at Height Regulations 2005 applies.†*

\* Paragraph (5)(e) substituted by SI 2007/320, regulation 48(2), Schedule 5.

† Paragraph (5)(f) inserted by SI 2005/735, regulation 17.

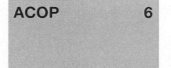

**Guidance**     6

## Inspection

80   When work equipment is first installed, and when it is moved or relocated, it must be inspected to make sure that it has been correctly installed and is operating safely. Where it is possible that the equipment is exposed to conditions that could cause it to deteriorate, it must be inspected regularly.

81   Inspection does not normally include the checks that are a part of the maintenance activity although certain aspects may be common. For the purpose of this regulation, inspection does not include a pre-use check that an operator makes before using the work equipment. While inspections need to be recorded, pre-use checks do not.

**ACOP**     6

## Identifying what needs to be inspected

**82   Where the risk assessment under regulation 3 of the Management Regulations has identified a significant risk to the operator or other workers from the installation or use of the work equipment, a suitable inspection should be carried out.**

**Guidance**     6

## Significant risk

83   A significant risk is one which could result in an imminent failure, which could lead to a major injury, as a result of:

(a)   incorrect installation or re-installation;
(b)   deterioration;
(c)   exceptional circumstances which could affect the safe operation of the work equipment.

84   Specified injuries are listed in the Reporting of Injuries, Diseases and Dangerous Occurrences Regulations 2013, *Reporting accidents and incidents at work: A brief guide to the Reporting of Injuries, Diseases and Dangerous Occurrences Regulations 2013 (RIDDOR)*[22] or see www.hse.gov.uk/riddor.

## Purpose of an inspection

85   The purpose of an inspection is to identify whether the equipment can be operated, adjusted and maintained safely and that any deterioration (for example defect, damage, wear) can be detected and remedied before it results in unacceptable risks.

**ACOP 6**

## What should be included in the inspection

**86    The extent of the inspection required will depend on the potential risks from the work equipment. Inspection should include, where appropriate, visual checks, functional checks and testing.**

**Guidance 6**

87    An inspection will vary from a simple visual external inspection to a detailed comprehensive inspection, which may include some dismantling and/or testing. An inspection should always include those safety-related parts necessary for safe operation of equipment, for example overload warning devices and limit switches. The extent of the inspection required will depend on:

(a)    the type of equipment;
(b)    where it is used;
(c)    how it is used.

88    Some work equipment will need examinations and thorough examinations under other legislation such as the Pressure Systems Safety Regulations 2000,[23] COSHH, Control of Lead at Work Regulations 2002,[24] Control of Asbestos Regulations 2012,[25] and LOLER. Inspections are only needed for such work equipment if these other examinations do not fully cover all the significant health and safety risks which are likely to arise from the use of the equipment, in a way that satisfies the requirements of PUWER.

### Testing

89    As part of an inspection, a functional or other test may be necessary to check that the safety-related parts, for example interlocks, protection devices, controls etc are working as intended and that the work equipment and relevant parts are structurally sound, for example non-destructive testing of safety-critical parts. The need for any testing (for example non-destructive testing of safety-critical parts) should be decided by the competent person who determines the nature of the inspection.

**ACOP 6**

### Competent persons

**90    You should ensure that people who determine the nature of the inspections required and who carry out inspections are competent to do so.**

**91    The competent person should have the necessary knowledge and experience.**

**Guidance 6**

92    *'Determining the nature of the inspection'* – the person who determines the extent of the inspection should have sufficient knowledge and experience, so that they can decide:

(a)    what the inspection should include;
(b)    how it should be done;
(c)    when it should be carried out.

Experienced, in-house employees such as a department manager or supervisor may be able to do this. They need to have sufficient experience and knowledge to be able to identify what needs to be inspected, and to be able to detect damage or faults resulting from deterioration. They should also be able to determine whether any tests are needed during the inspection to see if the equipment is working safely or is structurally sound.

93    *'Carrying out the inspection'* – the person who carries out the inspection does not need to be the same person who determines the nature of the inspections. The actual inspection can generally be done by an in-house employee with an adequate knowledge of the equipment to:

(a)    enable them to know what to look at (know the key components);
(b)    know what to look for (fault-finding);
(c)    know what to do (reporting faults, making a record, who to report to).

You should give them appropriate information, instruction and training so they can carry out the inspection properly and avoid danger.

94    The necessary level of competence will vary according to the type of equipment and where and how it is used. For some equipment, the level of competence to determine the nature of the inspections or even to carry them out may not be available in-house, in which case the help of another body with relevant competence will be needed. An example of this will be the person who carries out the annual inspection of some fairground rides under PUWER.

## Regulation 6(1) Installation

**95    Where work equipment is of a type where the safe operation is critically dependent on it being properly installed (or reinstalled), and where failure to carry this out would lead to a significant risk to the operator, or other worker, you should arrange for a suitable inspection to be carried out before it is put into service.**

96    Reinstallation includes assembling the equipment at a new site or in a new location. Equipment that has been installed or reinstalled is normally in a permanent or long-term location and is usually fixed in position. Installation or reinstallation does not normally include repositioning or moving equipment, particularly where there is no element of dismantling, reassembling and/or fixing the equipment in position, or if its location is transitory. Examples of work equipment where safety is critically dependent on the installation conditions include those where guarding is provided by presence-sensing devices (such as light curtains used for paper-cutting guillotines or pressure sensitive mats used with tube-bending machines). These devices allow free access to the danger zone but should be positioned so that if anyone approaches the danger zone they will be detected and the hazardous functions stopped before injury can occur.

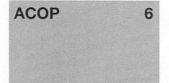

## Regulation 6(2) 'Conditions causing deterioration' and 'Dangerous situations'

**97    Where work equipment is of a type where the safe operation is critically dependent on its condition in use and deterioration would lead to a significant risk to the operator or other worker, you should arrange for suitable inspections to be carried out.**

## Equipment that should receive an inspection

98    The types of equipment whose use could result in significant risk as a result of deterioration and which may therefore need to be inspected include:

(a)    most fairground equipment;

Guidance 6

(b) machines where there is a need to approach the danger zone during normal operation such as horizontal injection moulding machines, paper-cutting guillotines, die-casting machines, shell-moulding machines;

(c) complex automated equipment;

(d) integrated production lines.

## Equipment for which an inspection is not required

99 If failure or fault of the equipment cannot lead to significant risk or if safety is guaranteed through appropriate maintenance regimes (under regulation 5), inspection may not be necessary. Equipment unlikely to need an inspection includes office furniture, hand tools, non-powered machinery and powered machinery such as a reciprocating fixed-blade metal cutting saw.

**ACOP 6**

## Frequency of inspection

**100 The frequency of inspections should be based on how quickly the work equipment or parts of it are likely to deteriorate and so give rise to a significant risk. This should take into account the type of equipment, how it is used and the conditions to which it is exposed.**

**Guidance 6**

101 The inspection frequency may be different for the same type of equipment because the rate of deterioration can vary in different situations. Where equipment is subject to frequent use in a harsh outdoor environment (for example at a coastal site or on a construction site), it is likely to need more frequent inspection than if it is used occasionally in an indoor environment such as a warehouse.

## Exceptional circumstances

102 Regulation 6(2) states that an inspection is necessary 'each time that exceptional circumstances which are liable to jeopardise the safety of the work equipment have occurred.' Exceptional circumstances which may result in the need for inspection include:

(a) major modifications, refurbishment or repair work;

(b) known or suspected serious damage;

(c) substantial change in the nature of use, for example from an extended period of inactivity.

## Regulation 6(3) Records

103 Records do not have to be kept in a particular form. They can be handwritten or stored electronically – from a pre-printed form to an entry in a diary. Although there are no legal requirements stating what they should contain, this is the sort of information you should include:

(a) information on the type and model of equipment;

(b) any identification mark or number;

(c) its normal location;

(d) the date that the inspection was carried out;

(e) who carried out the inspection;

(f) any faults;

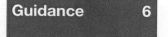

**Guidance** 6

(g)  any action taken;
(h)  to whom the faults have been reported;
(i)  the date when repairs or other necessary action were carried out.

**ACOP** 6

## Regulation 6(4) Physical evidence

**104  The physical evidence should be appropriate to the type of work equipment being inspected.**

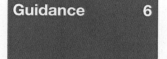

**Guidance** 6

105  For large items of equipment for which inspection is necessary, the physical evidence can be a copy of the record of the last inspection that was carried out. For smaller items of equipment, a tagging, colour coding or labelling system can be used. The purpose of the physical evidence is to help a user check easily:

(a)  if an inspection has been carried out;
(b)  whether or not it is current;
(c)  to determine the results of that inspection, by being able to link back from the physical evidence to the records.

## Regulation 6(5) What the regulation doesn't cover

106  These inspection requirements do not cover the following work equipment as set out in regulation 6(5):

(a)  Power presses covered by regulations 32–35 of PUWER. These include mechanically driven presses or press brakes (called 'power press(es)' in this book) which are power driven, have a flywheel and clutch, and which are wholly or partly used to work metal. A clutch, in relation to a power press, is a device to impart the movement of the flywheel to any tool when required.
(b)  Work equipment for lifting loads, including people. This is defined as work equipment for lifting or lowering loads and includes its attachments used for anchoring, fixing or supporting it. A load includes a person.
(c)  Under the Mines (Shafts and Winding) Regulations 1993,[26] winding apparatus means 'mechanically operated apparatus for lowering and raising loads through a (mine) shaft and includes a conveyance or counterweight attached to such apparatus and all ancillary apparatus'.
(d)  Work equipment required to be inspected by a competent person in accordance with regulation 31(4) or 32(2) of CDM, for example any work equipment and materials used for an excavation which affect its safety.
(e)  Inspection requirements for work equipment used for work at height are in regulation 12 of the Work at Height Regulations. Types of work equipment include: a guard rail, toe-board barrier or similar collective means of protection; working platforms that are fixed (eg a scaffold around a building) or mobile (eg a MEWP or scaffold tower); or a ladder.

---

### Summary of regulation 7

This regulation deals with restricting the use of some equipment to people who are trained in the use of that equipment and in the specific risks involved.

Having identified equipment that involves specific risk the employer also has to decide who can repair, modify, maintain or service it; and provide the appropriate training for those people.

---

# Regulation 7 Specific risks

**Regulation 7**

*(1)    Where the use of work equipment is likely to involve a specific risk to health or safety, every employer shall ensure that—*

*(a)    the use of that work equipment is restricted to those persons given the task of using it; and*

*(b)    repairs, modifications, maintenance or servicing of that work equipment is restricted to those persons who have been specifically designated to perform operations of that description (whether or not also authorised to perform other operations).*

*(2)    The employer shall ensure that the persons designated for the purposes of sub-paragraph (b) of paragraph (1) have received adequate training related to any operations in respect of which they have been so designated.*

**ACOP 7**

**107  You should ensure that, wherever possible, risks are always controlled by (in the order given):**

**(a)    eliminating the risks, or if that is not possible;**
**(b)    taking engineering (physical) measures to control the risks such as the provision of guards; but if the risks cannot be adequately controlled;**
**(c)    taking appropriate management measures to deal with the remaining risk, such as following safe systems of work and the provision of information, instruction and training.**

## Normal operation

**108  Where the risks from the use of work equipment cannot be adequately controlled by engineering measures such as guards or protection devices during its normal operation, it is particularly important that only the people whose task it is should be allowed to use the equipment. They should have received sufficient information, instruction and training to enable them to carry out the work safely.**

## Repairs, modifications etc

**109  Where the risks from the use of work equipment cannot be adequately controlled by engineering measures such as guards or protection devices during repair, maintenance, or other similar work, only people who have received sufficient information, instruction and training to enable them to carry out the work safely should do the work. They shall be the designated person for the purpose of this regulation.**

**Guidance 7**

110  Specific risks can be common to a particular class of work equipment. There can also be a specific risk associated with the way a particular item of work equipment is repaired, set or adjusted as well as with the way it is used.

111  The person whose normal work includes the use of a piece of work equipment will have been given 'the task of using it' and the instruction and training provided should be appropriate to that work. For example:

(a)    training of someone to use a grinding machine should cover the proper methods of dressing the abrasive wheels, see *Safety in the use of abrasive wheels*;[27]

**Guidance**    7

(b) in the case of someone carrying out a turning operation on a lathe, the training should cover the devices which should be used if working with emery cloth to obtain the required finish on a workpiece. The application of emery cloth, held directly by hand, should always be avoided. Further information on this topic can be found at hse.gov.uk/engineering.

112 The designated person to carry out repairs will be the person whose work includes these activities. This person could be the operator of the equipment, provided that they have received relevant instruction and training. For example, the training for a person who has to change the knives on guillotines should include any devices which could be used, such as knife handles, as well as the system of work.

## Specific risks to health

113 When looking at the risks from machinery it is easy to focus only on the safety risks. However, risks to the health of your workers from manual handling, dust, fumes, noise, hand/arm vibration etc are equally important, and should always be considered in your risk assessment.

---

**Summary of regulation 8**

There is a general duty in the HSW Act to provide employees and others, such as temporary workers supplied through an employment agency, with the information and instructions that are necessary to protect their health and safety – regulation 8 supplements that general duty.

It also links with the general requirement in the Management Regulations to provide information to employees relating to their health and safety. The Health and Safety (Consultation with Employees) Regulations 1996 (HSCER)[13] require employers to consult their employees on the information required under other regulations, including PUWER, about risks to their health and safety and preventative measures in place.

---

# Regulation 8 Information and instructions

**Regulation**    8

*(1) Every employer shall ensure that all persons who use work equipment have available to them adequate health and safety information and, where appropriate, written instructions pertaining to the use of the work equipment.*

*(2) Every employer shall ensure that any of his employees who supervises or manages the use of work equipment has available to him adequate health and safety information and, where appropriate, written instructions pertaining to the use of the work equipment.*

*(3) Without prejudice to the generality of paragraphs (1) or (2), the information and instructions required by either of those paragraphs shall include information and, where appropriate, written instructions on—*

*(a) the conditions in which and the methods by which the work equipment may be used;*
*(b) foreseeable abnormal situations and the action to be taken if such a situation were to occur; and*
*(c) any conclusions to be drawn from experience in using the work equipment.*

| Regulation | 8 |
|---|---|

*(4)    Information and instructions required by this regulation shall be readily comprehensible to those concerned.*

| Guidance | 8 |
|---|---|

## What the information and instructions should cover

114 Any information and written instructions you provide should cover:

(a)    the conditions in which the work equipment can be used;

(b)    the way in which the work equipment can be used;

(c)    any foreseeable difficulties that could arise, and instructions on how to deal with them;

(d)    using any conclusions drawn from experience using the work equipment, you should either record them or take steps to make sure that all appropriate members of the workforce are aware of them.

## Written instructions

115 Written instructions include the information provided by manufacturers or suppliers of work equipment such as instruction sheets or manuals, instruction placards, warning labels and training manuals. It can also include in-house instructions and instructions from training courses. There are duties on manufacturers and suppliers to provide sufficient information, including drawings, to enable the correct installation, safe operation and maintenance of the work equipment. Check that they are provided.

## Who needs to see the information and instructions

116 Ensure that any written instructions are available to the people, including any temporary workers, who directly use the work equipment. Make sure that instructions are available to other people who need them, for example maintenance instructions are made available or passed to the people involved in maintaining the work equipment.

117 Supervisors and managers should also have access to the information and written instructions. The amount of detailed health and safety information they will need to have immediately available for day-to-day running of production lines will vary, but it is important that they know what information is available and where it can be found.

## How the information and instructions should be made available

118 Information should be provided in writing, or verbally where that is considered sufficient. It is your responsibility to decide what is appropriate, taking into consideration the individual circumstances. Where there are complicated or unusual circumstances, the information should be in writing. Other factors that you should consider are:

(a)    the level of skill of the workers involved;

(b)    their experience and training;

(c)    the degree of supervision;

(d)    the complexity and length of the particular job.

**Guidance** 8

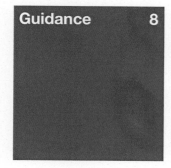

119  The information and written instructions should be easy to understand. They should be in plain English and/or other languages if that is more appropriate for the people using them. They should be set out in a logical order with illustrations where appropriate. Use standard symbols where appropriate.

120  Pay particular attention to any employees whose first language is not English, those with language difficulties or with disabilities which could make it difficult for them to receive or understand the information or instructions. You may need to make special arrangements in these cases, this could include, for example DVDs or translation into another language or the use of an interpreter.

---

**Summary of regulation 9**

Regulation 9 focuses on:
- providing training to people who use work equipment;
- providing training to employees who manage or supervise the use of work equipment;
- the need for separate driver training.

The information in paragraph 120 on information and instruction for employees (including temporary workers) whose first language is not English or who have other difficulties is also relevant for training.

---

# Regulation 9 Training

**Regulation** 9

> (1)  Every employer shall ensure that all persons who use work equipment have received adequate training for purposes of health and safety, including training in the methods which may be adopted when using the work equipment, any risks which such use may entail and precautions to be taken.
>
> (2)  Every employer shall ensure that any of his employees who supervises or manages the use of work equipment has received adequate training for purposes of health and safety, including training in the methods which may be adopted when using the work equipment, any risks which such use may entail and precautions to be taken.

**Guidance** 9

## What is 'adequate training'?

121  What constitutes 'adequate training' will vary depending on the job or activity and work equipment. You should determine the existing level of competence and provide training where necessary. You should:

(a)  evaluate the existing competence of employees and others such as temporary workers supplied by an employment agency to operate the full range of work equipment that they will use;

(b)  evaluate the competence they need to manage or supervise the use of work equipment;

(c)  train the employee and others (as in paragraph 121(a)) to make up any shortfall between their competence and that required to carry out the work with due regard to health and safety.

122  Take into account the circumstances in which the employee works. For example do they work alone or under the close supervision of a competent person?

## When is training necessary?

123 Training needs are likely to be greatest on recruitment. But training is also required:

(a) if the risks to which people are exposed change due to a change in their working tasks;
(b) because new technology or equipment is introduced;
(c) if the system of work changes.

124 You will need to provide refresher training when necessary. Skills decline if they are not used regularly. For example, you would want to check if refresher training is needed after a lengthy period of absence from work, or if a worker is moved onto a work process that has changed since they last performed those tasks. Pay particular attention to people who deputise for others infrequently – as they may need more frequent refresher training than those who do the job regularly.

## Training for young people

125 Training and proper supervision of young people is particularly important because of their relative immaturity and unfamiliarity with the working environment. Induction training is particularly important, because a young person will have little or no previous experience to draw on.

126 PUWER does not contain any specific requirements relating to the age of people using work equipment, since all employees should be competent to use work equipment with due regard to health and safety, regardless of their age. However, there is general guidance relevant to the provision and use of machinery under regulation 19 of the Management Regulations.

## The Management Regulations: Regulation 19 Protection of young persons

**Regulation 19**

*(1) Every employer shall ensure that young persons employed by him are protected at work from any risks to their health or safety which are a consequence of their lack of experience, or absence of awareness of existing or potential risks or the fact that young persons have not yet fully matured.*

*(2) Subject to paragraph (3), no employer shall employ a young person for work—*

*(a) which is beyond his physical or psychological capacity;*
*(b) involving harmful exposure to agents which are toxic or carcinogenic, cause heritable genetic damage or harm to the unborn child or which in any other way chronically affect human health;*
*(c) involving harmful exposure to radiation;*
*(d) involving the risk of accidents which it may reasonably be assumed cannot be recognised or avoided by young persons owing to their insufficient attention to safety or lack of experience or training; or*
*(e) in which there is a risk to health from—*
  *(i) extreme cold or heat;*
  *(ii) noise; or*
  *(iii) vibration,*

**Management Regulations**

**Regulation 19**

**Management Regulations**

*and in determining whether work will involve harm or risk for the purpose of this paragraph, regard shall be had to the results of the assessment.*

*(3)    Nothing in paragraph (2) shall prevent the employment of a young person who is no longer a child for work—*

*(a)    where it is necessary for his training;*
*(b)    where the young person will be supervised by a competent person; and*
*(c)    where any risk will be reduced to the lowest level that is reasonably practicable.*

**Guidance 9**

127  **Definitions of young people and children by age:**

(a)    **A young person** is anyone under 18.
(b)    **A child** is anyone who has not yet reached the official minimum school leaving age (MSLA). Pupils will reach the MSLA in the school year in which they turn 16.

128  The Management Regulations contain information for people who want to employ young people. You should assess risks to young people before they start work, taking into account their inexperience, lack of awareness of potential risks and their immaturity. You should provide information to parents of school-age children (for example when they are on work experience) about the risks and the control measures introduced and take account of the risk assessment in determining whether the young person should undertake certain work activities. There is guidance on the HSE website to help you if you are considering offering a work experience opportunity at www.hse.gov.uk/youngpeople/workexperience/cutting-bureaucracy.htm.

129  You do not have to carry out a separate risk assessment specifically for a young person. If you have not previously employed a young person you should review your existing risk assessment and take into account the specific factors for young people, before a young person starts work with you.

130  Competence and maturity are not simply a matter of the age of the worker. Training in itself will not ensure competence but it is part of what is required. The level of supervision needed will depend on how mature the workers are and whether they can work safely without putting themselves or others at risk. Even when they have been trained, young people may need more supervision to make sure that they do not act irresponsibly or take short cuts which put themselves and others at risk.

## When should training take place?

131  The Management Regulations specify that health and safety training should take place during working hours.

**ACOP 9**

## Driver training

**132  You should ensure that self-propelled work equipment, including any attachments or towed equipment, is only driven by workers who have received appropriate training in the safe driving of such work equipment.**

**ACOP** 9

## Chainsaw operators

**133 All workers who use a chainsaw should be competent to do so. Before using a chainsaw to carry out work on or in a tree, a worker should have received appropriate training and obtained a relevant certificate of competence or national qualification, unless they are undergoing such training and are adequately supervised. However, in the agricultural sector, this requirement only applies to first-time users of a chainsaw.**

**Guidance** 9

134 Everyone who uses a chainsaw at work, for whatever task, must have received adequate training under this regulation. The training should cover:

(a) dangers arising from the chainsaw itself;
(b) dangers arising from the task for which the chainsaw is to be used;
(c) the precautions to control these dangers, including relevant legal requirements.

135 Over and above this, due to the significant risks involved, if a chainsaw is to be used on or in a tree, the operator will be expected to hold a certificate of competence or national qualification relevant to the work they undertake.

136 The requirement for a certificate or award applies to people working with chainsaws on or in trees on agricultural holdings unless it is done as part of agricultural operations (for example, hedging, clearing fallen branches, or pruning trees to maintain clearance for machines etc) by the occupier or his employees and they have used a chainsaw before 5 December 1998.

## Chainsaw operators working in forestry and arboriculture

137 For professional chainsaw operators working in forestry and arboriculture the industry recommendation is that for 'high risk' activities the minimum level of adequacy of training is to a certificate of competence or nationally recognised qualification where assessment is carried out independently of the training. Table 1 lists examples of qualifications for activities deemed to be 'high risk'.

**Table 1 Qualifications for 'high risk' activities**

| Qualification title |
| --- |
| Level 2 Award in cross-cut timber using a chainsaw |
| Level 2 Award in chainsaw maintenance and cross-cutting |
| Level 2 Award in felling and processing trees up to 380 mm |
| Level 2 Award in remove branches and breakdown crowns using an chainsaw |
| Level 3 Award in severing uprooted or windblown trees using a chainsaw |
| Level 3 Award in assisted fell operations |
| Level 3 Award in emergency treework operations |
| Level 2 Award in accessing a tree using a rope and harness |
| Level 3 Award in aerial tree rescue operations |
| Level 3 Award in aerial cutting of trees with a chainsaw using free-fall techniques |
| Level 3 Award in aerial tree rigging |
| Level 3 Award in using a chainsaw from a mobile elevated work platform |

| | |
|---|---|
| **Guidance** | **9** |

For activities which are deemed to be 'low risk', risk assessment may be integrated into the training. Table 2 lists examples of qualifications for activities that are deemed to be 'low risk'.

**Table 2 Qualifications for 'low risk' activities**

| Qualification title |
|---|
| Level 2 Award in chainsaw maintenance |
| Level 3 Award in felling and processing trees over 380 mm |
| Level 2 Award in supporting colleagues undertaking off ground tree-related operations |
| Level 3 Award in preparing and agreeing emergency treework operations |
| Level 2 Award in using a powered pole pruner |
| Level 3 Award in aerial tree pruning |
| Level 3 Award in aerial cutting of trees using a crane |
| Level 3 Award in installation and maintenance of structural tree supports |
| Level 4 Award in thorough examination of arboricultural lifting equipment |

---

**Summary of regulation 10**

Everyone involved in the chain of supply of work equipment has legal obligations which are designed to ensure that new work equipment is safe. For example, section 6 of the HSW Act places general duties on designers, manufacturers, importers and suppliers to ensure this so far as is reasonably practicable.

Regulation 10 supplements the requirement of section 6 by placing a duty on the user of the work equipment.

---

# Regulation 10 Conformity with Community requirements

| | |
|---|---|
| **Regulation** | **10** |

(1)    Every employer shall ensure that an item of work equipment conforms at all times with any essential requirements, other than requirements which, at the time of its being first supplied or put into service in any place in which these Regulations apply, did not apply to work equipment of its type.

(2)    In this regulation "essential requirements", in relation to an item of work equipment, means requirements relating to the design and construction of work equipment of its type in any of the instruments listed in Schedule 1 (being instruments which give effect to Community directives concerning the safety of products).*

(3)    This regulation applies to items of work equipment provided for use in the premises or undertaking of the employer for the first time after 31st December 1992.

* Paragraphs (1) and (2) substituted by SI 2002/2174, regulation 7(a).

**Guidance**     **10**

138 Employers providing work equipment for use in the workplace should ensure that it has been made to the requirements of the legislation implementing any product Directive that is relevant to the equipment. This means that in addition to specifying that work equipment should comply with current health and safety legislation, you should also specify that it should comply with the legislation implementing any relevant EC Directive. You can check to see that the equipment bears a CE marking and is accompanied by the relevant certificates or declarations (ask for a copy of the EC Declaration of Conformity), as required by relevant product Directives.

139 You will need to check that appropriate operating instructions have been provided with the equipment and that there is information about residual hazards such as noise and vibration. You should also check the equipment for obvious faults. Your supplier should be able to give further advice about what the equipment is designed for and what it can and cannot be used for, or alternatively, make further enquiries with the manufacturer. There is further advice in HSE's leaflet *Buying new machinery*.[28]

---

**Summary of regulation 11**

Regulation 11(1) requires employers to take effective measures to prevent access to dangerous parts of machinery or stop their movement before any part of a person enters a danger zone.

Regulation 11(2) specifies the measures which you should take to prevent access to the dangerous parts of the machinery to achieve compliance with regulation 11(1).

Regulation 11(3) sets out various requirements for guards and protection devices.

Regulation 11(4) sets out requirements for protection appliances.

There are many HSE publications which contain specific guidance on a particular machine or industry. They describe the measures that can be taken to protect against risks associated with dangerous parts of machinery and these are available on HSE's website at www.hse.gov.uk.

---

## Regulation 11 Dangerous parts of machinery

**Regulation**     **11**

(1)   *Every employer shall ensure that measures are taken in accordance with paragraph (2) which are effective—*

(a)   *to prevent access to any dangerous part of machinery or to any rotating stock-bar; or*

(b)   *to stop the movement of any dangerous part of machinery or rotating stock-bar before any part of a person enters a danger zone.*

(2)   *The measures required by paragraph (1) shall consist of—*

(a)   *the provision of fixed guards enclosing every dangerous part or rotating stock-bar where and to the extent that it is practicable to do so, but where or to the extent that it is not, then*

(b)   *the provision of other guards or protection devices where and to the extent that it is practicable to do so, but where or to the extent that it is not, then*

(c)   *the provision of jigs, holders, push-sticks or similar protection appliances used in conjunction with the machinery where and to the extent that it is*

| Regulation | 11 |
|---|---|

*practicable to do so, and the provision of such information, instruction, training and supervision as is necessary.**

(3)   All guards and protection devices provided under sub-paragraphs (a) or (b) of paragraph (2) shall—

(a)   be suitable for the purpose for which they are provided;
(b)   be of good construction, sound material and adequate strength;
(c)   be maintained in an efficient state, in efficient working order and in good repair;
(d)   not give rise to any increased risk to health or safety;
(e)   not be easily bypassed or disabled;
(f)   be situated at sufficient distance from the danger zone;
(g)   not unduly restrict the view of the operating cycle of the machinery, where such a view is necessary;
(h)   be so constructed or adapted that they allow operations necessary to fit or replace parts and for maintenance work, restricting access so that it is allowed only to the area where the work is to be carried out and, if possible, without having to dismantle the guard or protection device.

(4)   All protection appliances provided under sub-paragraph (c) of paragraph (2) shall comply with sub-paragraphs (a) to (d) and (g) of paragraph (3).

(5)   In this regulation—

*"danger zone" means any zone in or around machinery in which a person is exposed to a risk to health or safety from contact with a dangerous part of machinery or a rotating stock-bar;*

*"stock-bar" means any part of a stock-bar which projects beyond the head-stock of a lathe.*

*Paragraph (2) substituted by SI 2002/2174, regulation 7(b).

| Guidance | 11 |
|---|---|

## Regulation 11(1)

140   You must take effective measures to prevent access to dangerous parts of machinery or stop their movement before any part of a person enters a danger zone. It also applies to contact with a rotating stock-bar which projects beyond the headstock of a lathe.

141   The term 'dangerous part' has been established in health and safety law through judicial decisions. In practice, this means that if a piece of work equipment could cause injury, while being used in a foreseeable way, it can be considered a dangerous part.

142   Protection against other hazards associated with machinery is dealt with in regulations 12 and 13. However, the measures required by this regulation may also protect or help to protect against those other hazards, such as ejected particles and heat.

## Preventing contact with dangerous parts of machinery

143   Appendix 1 gives more detailed information about the available methods of safeguarding which may be used to conform with regulation 11.

# Risk assessment

144  Your risk assessment carried out under regulation 3 of the Management Regulations should identify hazards presented by machinery. It should evaluate the nature of the injury, its severity and likelihood of occurrence for each hazard identified. This will enable you to decide whether the level of risk is acceptable or if risk reduction measures are needed. In most cases the objective of risk reduction measures is to prevent contact of part of the body or clothing with any dangerous part of the machine, for example guarding.

## Regulation 11(2)

145  Regulation 11(2) specifies the measures you must take to prevent access to the dangerous parts of the machinery and achieve compliance with regulation 11(1). The measures are ranked in the order they should be implemented, where practicable, to achieve an adequate level of protection. The levels of protection are:

(a)    fixed enclosing guards;
(b)    other guards or protection devices such as interlocked guards and pressure mats;
(c)    protection appliances such as jigs, holders and push-sticks etc.

Information, instruction, training and supervision will be needed regardless of the level of protection chosen.

146  An explanation of the guarding and protection terms used is given in Appendix 1.

147  The hazards from machinery should be identified as part of your risk assessment. The purpose of the risk assessment is to identify measures you can take to reduce the risks that the hazards present. When selecting measures, you should consider each level of protection from the first level of the scale listed in paragraph 145 and use measures from that level so far as it is practicable to do so, provided that they contribute to the reduction of risk. The selection process should continue down the scale until the combined measures are effective in reducing the risks to an acceptable level so meeting the requirements of regulation 11(1). In selecting the appropriate combination, you should take account of the requirements of the work, your evaluation of the risks, and the technical features of possible safeguarding solutions.

148  Most machinery will present more than one mechanical hazard, and you should deal with the risks associated with all of these. For example, at belt conveyors there is a risk of entanglement with the rotating shafts and of being trapped by the intake between drum and moving belt – so you should adopt appropriate safety measures.

149  Any risk assessment carried out under regulation 3 of the Management Regulations should not only deal with the machine when it is operating normally, but should also cover activities such as setting, maintenance, cleaning or repair. The assessment may indicate that these activities require a different combination of protective measures from those appropriate to the machine doing its normal work. In particular, parts of machinery that are not dangerous in normal use because they are not then accessible may become accessible and therefore dangerous while this type of work is being carried out.

150  Certain setting or adjustment operations which may have to be done with the machine running may require a greater reliance on the provision of information, instruction, training and supervision than for normal use.

**Guidance**     **11**

## Regulation 11(3) and regulation 11(4)

151 Regulation 11(3) sets out various requirements for guards and protection devices which are discussed in Appendix 1. Regulation 11(4) sets out requirements for protection appliances.

---

### Summary of regulation 12

Regulation 12 covers measures which employers have to take to prevent, control or minimise the effects of specified hazards during the use of work equipment. The hazards are listed in paragraph (3) of the regulation.

Examples of hazards that the regulation covers are:

- an article or substance falling from equipment, for example a loose board falling from scaffolding, a straw bale falling from a tractor foreloader or molten metal spilling from a ladle;
- an article or substance being ejected from equipment. This is where material held in the equipment is unexpectedly thrown out, for example swarf or workpiece ejected from a machine tool;
- rupture of parts of work equipment, for example an abrasive wheel bursting;
- disintegration or coming apart of parts of work equipment, such as the collapse of scaffolding or falsework;
- overheating or fire, due, for example to friction (bearings running hot, conveyor belt on jammed roller), electric motor burning out, thermostat failing, cooling system failure;
- explosion of the equipment due to pressure build-up, for example due to the failure of a pressure-relief valve or the unexpected blockage or sealing off of pipework;
- explosion of substances in the equipment, due, for example to exothermic chemical reaction or unplanned ignition of a flammable gas or vapour or finely divided organic material (for example flour, coal dust), or welding work on a container with flammable residues.

---

## Regulation 12 Protection against specified hazards

**Regulation**     **12**

   *(1)    Every employer shall take measures to ensure that the exposure of a person using work equipment to any risk to his health or safety from any hazard specified in paragraph (3) is either prevented, or, where that is not reasonably practicable, adequately controlled.*

   *(2)    The measures required by paragraph (1) shall—*

   *(a)    be measures other than the provision of personal protective equipment or of information, instruction, training and supervision, so far as is reasonably practicable; and*

   *(b)    include, where appropriate, measures to minimise the effects of the hazard as well as to reduce the likelihood of the hazard occurring.*

   *(3)    The hazards referred to in paragraph (1) are—*

   *(a)    any article or substance falling or being ejected from work equipment;*

   *(b)    rupture or disintegration of parts of work equipment;*

   *(c)    work equipment catching fire or overheating;*

   *(d)    the unintended or premature discharge of any article or of any gas, dust, liquid, vapour or other substance which, in each case, is produced, used or stored in the work equipment;*

**Regulation 12**

(e)   the unintended or premature explosion of the work equipment or any article or substance produced, used or stored in it.

(4)   For the purposes of this regulation "adequately" means adequately having regard only to the nature of the hazard and the nature and degree of exposure to the risk.

(5)   This regulation shall not apply where any of the following Regulations apply in respect of any risk to a person's health or safety for which such Regulations require measures to be taken to prevent or control such risk, namely—

(a)   the Ionising Radiations Regulations 1985;*
(b)   the Control of Asbestos Regulations 2006;†
(c)   the Control of Substances Hazardous to Health Regulations 1994;*
(d)   the Control of Noise at Work Regulations 2005;**
(e)   the Construction (Head Protection) Regulations 1989;
(f)   the Control of Lead at Work Regulations 1998;*
(g)   the Control of Vibration at Work Regulations 2005.††

* These regulations have been replaced by the Ionising Radiations Regulations 1999 (SI 1999/3232), the Control of Substances Hazardous to Health Regulations 2002 (SI 2002/2677, as amended by SI 2003/978 and SI 2004/3386) and the Control of Lead at Work Regulations 2002 (SI 2002/2676) respectively.

† Paragraph (5)(b) substituted by SI 2006/2739, regulation 36(2), Schedule 5.
** Paragraph (5)(d) substituted by SI 2005/1643, regulation 15.
†† Paragraph (5)(g) inserted by SI 2005/1093, regulation 13.

**Guidance 12**

152   Your risk assessment should identify if any of the hazards in regulation 12(3) are present in your workplace and assess the risks associated with them. You should consider how likely it is that any of these events might happen and the consequent danger if they do happen, to identify the measures you need to take.

153   Regulation 12(1) sets out the primary aim, which is to prevent any of the events in regulation 12(3) arising, if that event exposes people to risk. Where possible, the equipment should be designed so that events presenting a risk cannot happen. If this is not reasonably practicable, you should take steps to reduce the risk. Examples include the monitoring of solvent concentrations at evaporating ovens to detect the build-up of explosive atmospheres, or the use of inert gas systems to control and suppress dust explosions.

154   Regulation 12(1) allows the discharge or ejection of material as an intentional or unavoidable part of the process (for example grit-blasting of castings, sawdust from woodworking), but any risks to people must be controlled. The regulation also allows the use of equipment designed to make use of explosive forces in a controlled manner (for example an internal combustion engine or a rail detonator signal).

155   Equipment may have been designed before manufacture to eliminate or reduce the likelihood of the type of event listed in regulation 12(3). But equipment suppliers cannot control the materials used in equipment, or the environment in which it is used, and it is up to you to ensure that the equipment is suitable for their application, as required by regulation 4(2). Therefore risks associated with high temperature, vibration or a flammable atmosphere must be controlled.

156   Regulation 12(2)(a) requires that risk-controlling measures should be provided as part of the equipment, so far as is reasonably practicable. Provision and use of

**Guidance 12**

personal protective equipment may be appropriate where a risk remains that cannot be eliminated in some other way.

157 Regulation 12(2)(b) requires that in addition to reducing the likelihood of the event happening, measures must be taken to reduce the effect of any event which does give rise to risks. An example might be a blast wall or where there is a risk from a pressure-relief panel or vent bursting, ensuring that any gases or liquids discharged are directed to a safe place, contained, or made safe as appropriate.

158 Training, supervision and provision of information to users are all important. Firstly, they can help to ensure that equipment is operated in the correct way to avoid dangers happening. Secondly, they can help to ensure that the appropriate safeguards are taken to prevent people being exposed to risk.

## Abrasive wheels

159 A particular example of the application of these principles is the use of abrasive wheels.

(a)     To minimise the risk of bursting, abrasive wheels should always be run within the specified maximum rotation speed.

(b)     If there is enough room, this will be marked on the wheel (in accordance with regulation 23).

(c)     Smaller wheels should have a notice fixed in the workroom, giving the individual or class maximum permissible rotation speed.

(d)     The power-driven spindle should be governed so that its rotation speed does not exceed this.

(e)     Guarding must be provided to contain fragments of the wheel that might fly off if it did burst, to prevent them injuring anyone in the workplace. The guarding has an additional role in helping to meet the requirements of regulation 11; it should be designed, constructed and maintained to fulfil both functions.

(f)     Providing information and training for workers in the correct handling and mounting of abrasive wheels (including pre-mounting and storing procedures) is also important to reduce the risk of bursting.

## Relationship with other legislation

160 Regulation 12(5) refers to other regulations which cover specific hazards. For example, COSHH would apply to leakage of a toxic substance, whereas regulation 12 would apply to leakage of steam or cooling water from the same equipment. Similarly, COSHH would apply to the discharge of coolant mist from a machine tool, but regulation 12 would apply in the case of ejected swarf.

---

### Summary of regulation 13

Many items of equipment have exposed surfaces, or contain or use hot or very cold substances. Regulation 13 deals with the risks from these and looks at the measures you can take to reduce the risk of injury to people coming into contact with hot or very cold work equipment, parts of work equipment or articles or substances in the work equipment. It does not cover any related risk such as radiant heat or glare.

---

# Regulation 13 High or very low temperature

| Regulation | 13 |
|---|---|

*Every employer shall ensure that work equipment, parts of work equipment and any article or substance produced, used or stored in work equipment which, in each case, is at a high or very low temperature shall have protection where appropriate so as to prevent injury to any person by burn, scald or sear.*

| Guidance | 13 |
|---|---|

161 Accessible surfaces of equipment or machinery, when hot or very cold, represent sources of risk of burn or other injury such as frostbite. Examples of relevant equipment might include a flat-iron, foundry equipment, drop forging, hot pressing, liquid nitrogen tank, gas cooker, blast furnace, snow-making machine, cold store, steam pipe etc. Employees may have to work close to such equipment. Touching such surfaces may take place intentionally, for example to operate a handle of the equipment, or unintentionally, when someone is near the equipment.

162 Where it is possible to apply engineering protective measures, for example by reducing the risk from contact with hot surface temperatures by insulation, shielding, barricading or guarding, you should adopt these in preference to personal protective measures. The risk from hot process materials – contact, splashing, spilling etc – should likewise be reduced by limiting maximum temperature, limiting liquor level, indirect steam heating methods, provision of doors, lids or covers, temperature interlocking of doors or lids and deflection systems for hot liquor (catch pan, spillway etc). You will need to decide the choice of protective measures in each particular case and according to the particular circumstances.

163 In some cases, surfaces of equipment or devices have to be hot and accessible to operate, for example cooker hotplates, soldering iron bit, heated rolls. While the regulation says that engineering protective measures should be taken in preference to others, it recognises that this is not always possible. Alternative methods include the provision and use of personal protective equipment and/or organisational measure. This includes:

(a)　training;
(b)　warning signs (warning signals, visual and noise alarm signals);
(c)　supervision;
(d)　operating instructions/instructions for use.

---

### Summary of regulation 14

Regulation 14 addresses the risks to health and safety created by the starting or uncontrolled operation of work equipment.

It covers the need for one or more controls for starting work equipment. And why, apart from automatic equipment, equipment should never start or change its operating conditions unintentionally.

Restarting or changing operating conditions as a result of the normal operating cycle of an automatic device is not covered by this regulation.

---

# Regulation 14 Controls for starting or making a significant change in operating conditions

**Regulation**     **14**

*(1)     Every employer shall ensure that, where appropriate, work equipment is provided with one or more controls for the purposes of—*

*(a)     starting the work equipment (including re-starting after a stoppage for any reason); or*

*(b)     controlling any change in the speed, pressure or other operating conditions of the work equipment where such conditions after the change result in risk to health and safety which is greater than or of a different nature from such risks before the change.*

*(2)     Subject to paragraph (3), every employer shall ensure that, where a control is required by paragraph (1), it shall not be possible to perform any operation mentioned in sub-paragraph (a) or (b) of that paragraph except by a deliberate action on such control.*

*(3)     Paragraph (1) shall not apply to re-starting or changing operating conditions as a result of the normal operating cycle of an automatic device.*

**Guidance**     **14**

164  It should only be possible to start the equipment by using appropriate controls. Operating the control need not necessarily immediately start the equipment as control systems may require certain conditions (for example those relating to operation or protection devices) to be met before starting can be achieved.

165  Restarting the equipment after any stoppage is subject to the same requirements. The stoppage may have been deliberate or may have happened, for example by the activation of a protection device. Operators should not normally be able to restart the equipment simply by resetting a protection device such as, for example, an interlock or a person's withdrawal from an area covered by a sensing device – operation of the start control should also be required.

166  Any change in the operating conditions of the equipment should only be possible by the use of a control unless the change does not increase risks to health and safety. Examples of operating conditions include speed, pressure, temperature and power. For example, certain multifunctional machines are used in the metalworking industry for punching or shearing metal using different tools located on different parts of the machines. Safety in the use of these machines is achieved by means of a combination of safe systems of work and physical safeguards which match the characteristics of the workpiece. It is essential that the function of the machine (for example punching or shearing) is changed by a conscious, positive action by the operator and that unused parts of the machine cannot start up unintentionally.

## Regulation 14(1)(b) and 14(2)

167  The purpose of regulation 14(1)(b) and 14(2) is to ensure that users or other people are not caught unawares by any changes in the operating conditions or modes of the equipment in use.

**Guidance**     14

### Regulation 14(3)

168 Regulation 14(3) acknowledges that in the case of automatic machinery such as those controlled by programmable electronic systems, it is not appropriate to require separate controls for changing operating conditions when such changes are part of the normal operating cycle. (Nevertheless, these machines should be safeguarded as required by regulations 11 and 12.) However, where interventions outside the normal sequence, such as clearing blockages, setting or cleaning, proper controls in accordance with regulations 14(1) and (2) should be provided.

169 The start control can be separate, combined with controls for operating conditions, or more than one of each type of control can be provided. The controls can be combined with stop controls as required by regulation 15 but not with an emergency stop control provided in accordance with regulation 16. 'Hold-to-run' devices are examples of combined stop and start controls. These should be designed so that the stop function has priority following the release of the control.

170 The controls provided should be designed and positioned to prevent inadvertent or accidental operation. Buttons or levers, for example, should have an appropriate shrouding or locking facility. It should not be possible for the control to 'operate itself', for example due to the effects of gravity, vibration or failure of a spring mechanism. Starting that is initiated from a keyboard or other multifunction device should require some form of confirmation in addition to the start command, and the results of the actuation should be displayed.

---

**Summary of regulation 15**

Regulation 15 deals with controls for ensuring that work equipment being operated under normal conditions can be stopped without risk to health and safety. Stopping work equipment may involve a number of coordinated operations that have to be brought under control to avoid risk to health and safety.

---

## Regulation 15 Stop controls

**Regulation**     15

*(1)   Every employer shall ensure that, where appropriate, work equipment is provided with one or more readily accessible controls the operation of which will bring the work equipment to a safe condition in a safe manner.*

*(2)   Any control required by paragraph (1) shall bring the work equipment to a complete stop where necessary for reasons of health and safety.*

*(3)   Any control required by paragraph (1) shall, if necessary for reasons of health and safety, switch off all sources of energy after stopping the functioning of the work equipment.*

*(4)   Any control required by paragraph (1) shall operate in priority to any control which starts or changes the operating conditions of the work equipment.*

**Guidance**     15

171 Regulation 15(1) requires that the action of the stop control should bring the equipment to a safe condition in a safe manner. This acknowledges that it is not always desirable to bring all items of work equipment immediately to a complete stop if this could result in other risks. If needed, to ensure the safety of the operator, it is acceptable that the operation of the stop control brings the equipment to rest in sequence or at the end of an operating cycle.

**Guidance** **15**

172 Regulation 15(2) is qualified by 'where necessary for reasons of health and safety'. Therefore all accessible dangerous parts must be rendered stationary which may mean they need to be locked into position and may be allowed to idle. However, parts of equipment which do not present a risk, such as suitably guarded cooling fans, do not need to be positively stopped.

173 Regulation 15(3) requires that the control should switch off all sources of energy from the equipment, after it has stopped, if this is necessary to prevent or minimise risk to health or safety. Where it is necessary to retain power for production reasons and a hazard could arise due to unexpected movement giving rise to risk of injury, control systems should be designed to immediately remove the power, should such an event occur. Where internally stored energy could lead to risk, it should be cut off by the action of the stop control. For example, horizontal plastic injection moulding machines may store hydraulic energy in internal hydraulic reservoirs which, under certain fault conditions, may cause unintentional movements which could cause injury. In this case, the stop control should effectively isolate or dissipate the stored energy to ensure safety.

174 The stop control should take priority over any operating or start control. Where possible, it should not require anything other than a short manual action to activate it, even though the stop and disconnection sequence that is initiated may take some time to complete. Further information on the categories of stop function can be found in BS EN 60204-1.[29] Although this standard (which deals with specifications for general requirements for an individual machine) applies to new machinery, it gives valuable guidance which may be useful for any equipment – new or used.

---

**Summary of regulation 16**

Regulation 16 deals with:

- the number of emergency stop controls;
- the accessibility of those controls;
- interaction with other controls required by regulation 15;
- circumstances where emergency stop controls are not necessary;
- the priority given to emergency stop controls.

The main purpose of an emergency stop control is that it is simple to locate and operate, regardless of the type of control that you employ. Guidance on the specific features of emergency stop controls is available in national, European and international standards.

---

## Regulation 16 Emergency stop controls

**Regulation** **16**

(1)    Every employer shall ensure that, where appropriate, work equipment is provided with one or more readily accessible emergency stop controls unless it is not necessary by reason of the nature of the hazards and the time taken for the work equipment to come to a complete stop as a result of the action of any control provided by virtue of regulation 15(1).

(2)    Any control required by paragraph (1) shall operate in priority to any control required by regulation 15(1).

**Guidance** **16**

175 An emergency stop control should be provided where the other safeguards in place are not adequate to prevent risk when an irregular event occurs. However, an emergency stop control should not be considered as a substitute for safeguarding.

**Guidance 16**

176 Where it is appropriate to have one, based on the risk assessment, an emergency stop should be provided at every control point and at other appropriate locations around the equipment so that action can be taken quickly. The location of emergency stop controls should be determined as a follow-up to the risk assessment required under the Management Regulations. Although it is desirable that emergency stops rapidly bring work equipment to a halt, this must be achieved under control in order not to create any additional hazards.

177 Emergency stops are provided to enable a rapid response to potentially dangerous situations, they should not be used to stop the equipment during normal operation.

178 If emergency stop controls are considered necessary, they should be easy to reach and easy to use.

---

**Summary of regulation 17**

This regulation deals with the controls for work equipment, including:
- ensuring that the purpose of the control is clearly identifiable;
- the location of the controls so that neither the operator nor any other person near the equipment is at risk;
- the use in particular circumstances of warnings to signal the use of equipment controls, as required by regulation 24;
- giving advance warning to people exposed to risk;
- giving people exposed to risk the means of avoiding it.

---

# Regulation 17 Controls

**Regulation 17**

*(1) Every employer shall ensure that all controls for work equipment are clearly visible and identifiable, including by appropriate marking where necessary.*

*(2) Except where necessary, the employer shall ensure that no control for work equipment is in a position where any person operating the control is exposed to a risk to his health or safety.*

*(3) Every employer shall ensure where appropriate—*

*(a) that, so far as is reasonably practicable, the operator of any control is able to ensure from the position of that control that no person is in a place where he would be exposed to any risk to his health or safety as a result of the operation of that control, but where or to the extent that it is not reasonably practicable;*

*(b) that, so far as is reasonably practicable, systems of work are effective to ensure that, when work equipment is about to start, no person is in a place where he would be exposed to a risk to his health or safety as a result of the work equipment starting, but where neither of these is reasonably practicable;*

*(c) that an audible, visible or other suitable warning is given by virtue of regulation 24 whenever work equipment is about to start.*

*(4) Every employer shall take appropriate measures to ensure that any person who is in a place where he would be exposed to a risk to his health or safety as a result of the starting or stopping of work equipment has sufficient time and suitable means to avoid that risk.*

| Guidance | 17 |
|---|---|

## Regulation 17(1)

179  It should be possible to identify easily what each control does and on which equipment it takes effect. Both the controls and their markings should be clearly visible. As well as having legible wording or symbols, factors such as the colour, shape and position of controls are important; a combination of these can often be used to reduce ambiguity. Some controls may need to be distinguishable by touch, for example inching buttons on printing machines. Few controls will be adequately identifiable without some sort of marking.

180  The marking and form of many controls is covered by national, European and international standards either generic or specific to the type of equipment (BS 3641).[30] However, additional marking may be desirable.

## Regulation 17(2)

181  Controls used in the normal running of the equipment should normally not be placed where anybody using them might be exposed to risk. However, controls used for setting-up and fault-finding procedures may have to be positioned where people are at some risk, for example on a robot-teaching pendant. In such cases particular precautions should be employed to ensure safety; examples include using hold-to-run controls, enabling controls and emergency stop controls. Further precautions include the selection of reduced/limited capability of the work equipment during such operations.

## Regulation 17(3)(a)

182  The provisions of regulation 17(3)(a) apply where physical safeguarding methods employed in accordance with regulation 11(2)(a) and (b) do not completely prevent access to dangerous parts of work equipment, or where people are at risk from other aspects of the operation, eg noise, or harmful radiation. The preferred aim is to position controls so that operators of equipment are able to see from the control position that no one is at risk from anything they set going. To be able to do this, operators need to have a view of any part of the equipment that may put anyone at risk. A direct view is best, but supplementing by mirrors or more sophisticated visual or sensing facilities may be necessary.

183  There will normally be little difficulty in meeting this requirement in the case of small and compact equipment. With larger equipment there is normally some latitude in the positioning of controls, and the safety aspect should be considered in deciding their location; this would apply, for example, on large process plant such as newspaper printing machinery or chemical plant.

184  Where people are at risk from dangerous parts of machinery, normal safeguarding procedures should restrict the need for surveillance to vulnerable areas; an example would be on large newspaper printing machines. However, where regular intervention is necessary, which involves entry into, removal of, or opening of safeguards, for example for maintenance purposes, interlocks or similar devices may be necessary as appropriate to prevent start-up while people are at risk. Additional measures may be needed to ensure that people do not remain inside safeguards at start-up. Similarly, where sensing devices are employed to aid surveillance, they may be interlocked with the controls so as to prevent start-up when people are at risk.

185  If anyone other than the operator is also working on the equipment, they may use permissive start controls. Such controls can indicate to the operator that

everyone is clear and permit a start. These can be located at a position of safety from where they can make sure that no one is at risk.

186  Where there is a risk other than from dangerous parts of machinery (for example noise, radiation etc), people at some distance from the work equipment may be affected. In such circumstances, it may not always be reasonably practicable for operators to have sight of all parts of the work equipment so it may be necessary to employ systems of work or warning devices. Warning devices only provide limited protection and additional measures may be required if the risks are high. For example, it would not be acceptable to rely on audible or visible alarms where the risk is of an imminent potentially fatal dose of ionising radiation, but they may be adequate where the risk is from noisy plant.

## Regulation 17(3)(b)

187  If the nature of the installation is such that it is not reasonably practicable for the operator at the control position to ensure that no one is at risk, then a system of work must be devised and used to achieve that aim. This should implement procedures to eliminate or reduce the probability of any workers being at risk as a result of starting-up. An example is systems using signallers; these are often used to help crane drivers, or tractor drivers setting a manned harvester in motion.

## Regulation 17(3)(c)

188  The warning should comply with regulation 24, that means it should be unambiguous, easily perceived and easily understood. Signals may be visual, audible, tactile or a combination of the three, as appropriate.

## Regulation 17(4)

189  Warnings given in accordance with regulation 17(3)(c) should be given sufficiently in advance of the equipment actually starting to give those at risk time to get clear or take suitable actions to prevent risks. This may take the form of a device by means of which the person at risk can prevent start-up or warn the operator of their presence.

190  The provisions of regulation 17 do not preclude people from remaining in positions where they are at risk. Their aim is to prevent an operator unintentionally placing people at risk. Regulation 11, in its hierarchical approach to safeguarding, recognises that in exceptional circumstances people may have to approach dangerous parts of machinery, such as for maintenance purposes. Access to such positions should only be allowed under strictly controlled conditions and in accordance with regulation 11.

---

**Summary of regulation 18**

Regulation 18 deals with:
- taking realistic and practical allowances into account when choosing or specifying control systems;
- not increasing risk when the control system is operating, either directly or indirectly, by impeding the operation of other safety measures; not increasing risk if a control system fails or loses its power supply.

---

# Regulation 18 Control systems

**Regulation 18**

*(1) Every employer shall ensure, so far as is reasonably practicable, that all control systems of work equipment—*

*(a) are safe; and*

*(b) are chosen making due allowance for the failures, faults and constraints to be expected in the planned circumstances of use.\**

*(2) Without prejudice to the generality of paragraph (1), a control system shall not be safe unless—*

*(a) its operation does not create any increased risk to health or safety;*

*(b) it ensures, so far as is reasonably practicable, that any fault in or damage to any part of the control system or the loss of supply of any source of energy used by the work equipment cannot result in additional or increased risk to health or safety;*

*(c) it does not impede the operation of any control required by regulation 15 or 16.*

\* Paragraph (1) substituted by SI 2002/2174, regulation 7(c).

**Guidance 18**

191 A control system can be defined as: 'a system or device which responds to input signals and generates an output signal which causes the equipment under control to operate in a particular manner.'

192 The input signals may be made by an operator via a manual control, or from the equipment itself, for example from automatic sensors or protection devices (photoelectric guards, guard interlock devices, speed limiters etc). Signals from the equipment may also include information (feedback) on the condition of the equipment and its response (position, whether it is running, speed).

193 Failure of any part of the control system or its power supply should lead to a 'fail-safe' condition. Fail-safe can be more correctly and realistically called 'minimised failure to danger'. This should not impede the operation of the 'stop' or 'emergency stop' controls. The measures which should be taken in the design and application of a control system to mitigate against the effects of its failure will need to be balanced against the consequences of any failure. The greater the risk, the more resistant the control system should be to the effects of failure. Bringing a machine to a safe halt may achieve the objective. Halting a chemical process, however, could create further hazards. Care should be taken to fully assess the consequences of such events and provide further protection, for example standby power plant or diverting chemicals to a place of safety. It should always be possible to recover to a safe condition.

194 There are national, European and international standards (BS EN 60204-1, BS EN ISO 13849-1[31] BS EN 62061)[32] which provide guidance on design of control systems so as to achieve high levels of performance related to safety. Though they are aimed at new machinery, they may be used as guidance for existing work equipment.

**Summary of regulation 19**

The aim of this regulation is to allow equipment to be made safe under particular circumstances, such as when maintenance is to be carried out, when an unsafe condition develops (failure of a component, overheating, or pressure build-up), or where a temporarily adverse environment would render the equipment unsafe, for example electrical equipment in wet conditions or in a flammable or explosive atmosphere.

# Regulation 19 Isolation from sources of energy

**Regulation**     **19**

(1)　Every employer shall ensure that where appropriate work equipment is provided with suitable means to isolate it from all its sources of energy.

(2)　Without prejudice to the generality of paragraph (1), the means mentioned in that paragraph shall not be suitable unless they are clearly identifiable and readily accessible.

(3)　Every employer shall take appropriate measures to ensure that re-connection of any energy source to work equipment does not expose any person using the work equipment to any risk to his health or safety.

**Guidance**     **19**

195 Equipment must be capable of being isolated from all its sources of energy. For this reason control measures such as interlocked guards and emergency stop controls are not suitable as a means of isolation. The most common sources of energy are power, heat and pressure but depending on the particular type of equipment there may be others that you will need to take into account when carrying out your risk assessment.

196 Isolation means establishing a break in the energy supply in a secure manner, ie by ensuring that inadvertent reconnection is not possible. You should identify the possibilities and risks of reconnection as part of your risk assessment, which should then establish how secure isolation can be achieved. For some equipment, this can be done by simply removing the plug from the electrical supply socket. For other equipment, an isolating switch or valve may have to be locked in the off or closed position to avoid unsafe reconnection. The closed position is not always the safe position: for example, drain or vent outlets may need to be secured in the open position.

197 If work on isolated equipment is being done by more than one person, it may be necessary to provide a locking device with multiple locks and keys. Each will have their own lock or key, and all locks have to be taken off before the isolating device can be removed. Keys should not be passed to anyone other than the nominated personnel and should not be interchanged between nominated people.

198 For safety reasons in some circumstances sources of energy should be maintained when the equipment is stopped, for example when the power supply is helping to keep the equipment or parts of it safe. In such cases, isolation could lead to consequent danger, so it will be necessary to take appropriate measures to eliminate any risk before attempting to isolate the equipment.

199 You should provide means of isolation where the work equipment is dependent on external energy sources such as electricity, pressure (hydraulic or pneumatic) or heat. Where possible, means of dissipating stored energy should be provided. Other sources of energy such as its potential energy, chemical or radiological energy, cannot be isolated from the equipment. Nevertheless, there

**Guidance    19**

should be a means of preventing such energy from adversely affecting workers, by shielding, barriers or restraint.

200  Isolation of electrical equipment is dealt with by regulation 12 of the Electricity at Work Regulations 1989.[33]

201  Thermal energy may be supplied by circulation of preheated fluid such as water or steam. In such cases, isolating valves should be fitted to the supply pipework.

202  Similar provision should be made for energy supplies in the form of liquids or gases under pressure. A planned preventive maintenance programme should be in place which assures effective means of isolation. It may be necessary to isolate pipework by physically disconnecting it or fitting spades in the line to provide the necessary level of protection. Redundancy in the form of more than one isolation valve fitted in series may also be used, but care should be taken to check the efficacy of each valve function periodically. The performance of such valves may deteriorate over time, and their effectiveness often cannot be judged visually.

203  The energy source of some equipment is held in the substances contained within it; examples are the use of gases or liquids as fuel, electrical accumulators (batteries) and radionuclides. In such cases, isolation may mean removing the energy-containing material, although this may not always be necessary.

204  It is not appropriate to isolate the terminals of a battery from the chemical cells within it, as that could not be done without destroying the whole unit.

205  Some equipment makes use of natural sources of energy such as light or flowing water. In such cases, suitable means of isolation include screening from light, and the means of diverting water flow, respectively. Another natural energy source, wind power, is less easily diverted, so sail mechanisms should be designed and constructed so as to permit minimal energy transfer when necessary. Effective restraint should be provided to prevent unintentional movement when taken out of use for repair or maintenance.

206  Regulation 19(3) requires precautions to ensure that people are not put at risk following reconnection of the energy source. So, reconnection of the energy source should not put people at risk by itself initiating movement or other hazard. Measures are also required to ensure that guards and other protection devices are functioning correctly before operation begins.

---

**Summary of regulation 20**

Many types of equipment could topple over, overturn or collapse unless they are securely fixed. Regulation 20 explains how equipment should be stabilised, clamped, tied or fastened to make it safe.

---

## Regulation 20 Stability

**Regulation    20**

*Every employer shall ensure that work equipment or any part of work equipment is stabilised by clamping or otherwise where necessary for purposes of health or safety.*

**Guidance    20**

207  The regulation applies to both fixed work equipment and mobile work equipment. Where ballasting or counterbalancing is employed for mobile work equipment, the stabilising method should be reviewed each time the equipment is repositioned.

208 Most machines used in a fixed position should be bolted or otherwise fastened down so that they do not move or rock during use. This can be done by fastening the equipment to an appropriate foundation or supporting structure. Other means include lashing or tying to a supporting structure or platform.

209 Where the stability of the work equipment is not inherent in its design or operation or where it is mounted in a position where its stability could be compromised, for example by severe weather conditions, additional measures should be taken to ensure its stability.

210 Certain types of mobile work equipment, for example access platforms, while inherently stable, can have their stability increased during use by means of outriggers or similar devices. While this equipment cannot be 'clamped' or 'fixed', steps should be taken to ensure that the equipment is always used within the limits of its stability at any given time.

## Strength and stability of lifting equipment

211 Specific information on securing the stability of lifting equipment is set out in regulation 4 of LOLER.

---

**Summary of regulation 21**

Any place where a person uses work equipment should be suitably and sufficiently lit. If the ambient lighting provided in the workplace is suitable and sufficient for the tasks involved in the use of the equipment, special lighting won't be needed. This regulation looks at areas where additional lighting may be required.

---

# Regulation 21 Lighting

*Every employer shall ensure that suitable and sufficient lighting, which takes account of the operations to be carried out, is provided at any place where a person uses work equipment.*

212 This regulation complements the requirement for sufficient and suitable workplace lighting in the Workplace Regulations and the Electricity at Work Regulations 1989.[33]

213 Lighting should be adequate for the needs of the task.

214 You should provide local lighting on the machine for the illumination of the work area when the construction of the machine and/or its guards make the normal lighting inadequate for the safe and efficient operation of the machine, for example on sewing machines. Local lighting may be needed to give sufficient view of a dangerous process or to reduce visual fatigue. Travelling cranes may obscure overhead lighting for the driver and others, particularly when there is no natural light available (such as when people are working at night), and supplementary lighting may be necessary.

215 You should also provide additional lighting in areas not covered by general lighting when work, such as maintenance or repairs, for example, is carried out in them. The arrangements for the provision of lighting could be temporary, by means of hand or other portable lights. This solution could be useful for lighting inside enclosures, such as lift shafts. The standard of lighting required will be related to the purpose for which the work equipment is used or to the work being carried out.

**Guidance 21**

Lighting levels should be checked periodically to ensure that the intensity is not diminished by dust and grime deposits. Where necessary, you should clean luminaires and reflectors at regular intervals to maintain lighting efficiency.

216 Where access is foreseeable on an intermittent but regular basis, you should always consider providing permanent lighting.

---

**Summary of regulation 22**

Regulation 5 requires that equipment is maintained. Regulation 22 requires that equipment is constructed or adapted in a way that takes account of the risks associated with carrying out maintenance work, such as routine and planned preventive maintenance, as described in the guidance to regulation 5.

The design of equipment in relation to maintenance work on it may also be affected by other legislation. In particular, electrically powered equipment is subject to the Electricity at Work Regulations 1989 relating to risks of injury from electric shock or burn, or from explosion or ignition initiated by electricity. Guidance on those Regulations includes details of relevant equipment requirements.

---

## Regulation 22 Maintenance operations

**Regulation 21**

*Every employer shall take appropriate measures to ensure that work equipment is so constructed or adapted that, so far as is reasonably practicable, maintenance operations which involve a risk to health or safety can be carried out while the work equipment is shut down, or in other cases—*

*(a) maintenance operations can be carried out without exposing the person carrying them out to a risk to his health or safety; or*

*(b) appropriate measures can be taken for the protection of any person carrying out maintenance operations which involve a risk to his health or safety.*

**Guidance 22**

217 Compliance with this regulation will help to ensure that when maintenance work is carried out, it is possible to do it safely and without risk to health, as required by Section 2 of the HSW Act; it will also help to comply with regulation 5(1), since 'used' includes maintained. Regulation 11(3)(h) contains a requirement linked to regulation 22, but focusing on the narrower aspect of the design of guards for such work. Many accidents have occurred during maintenance work, often as a result of failure to adapt the equipment to reduce the risk.

218 In most cases the need for safe maintenance will have been considered at the design stage and attended to by the manufacturer, and you should just review the measures provided. In other cases, particularly when a range of interconnecting components may be put together, for example in a research laboratory or a production line, you should consider when carrying out your risk assessment whether any extra features should be incorporated so that maintenance can be done safely and without risks to health.

219 Ideally, there is no risk associated with the maintenance operation. For example, lubrication points on machines may be designed so that they can be accessed safely even while the machine is in motion, or adjustment points positioned so they can be used without opening guards.

220 If, however, the maintenance work involves a risk, this regulation requires that the installation should be designed so the work can, so far as is reasonably

**Guidance     22**

practicable, be carried out with the equipment stopped or inactive. This will probably be the case for most equipment.

221 If equipment has to be running or working during a maintenance operation and this presents risks, you should take measures to enable the operation of the equipment in a way that reduces the risk. These measures include further safeguards or functions designed into the equipment, such as limiting the power, speed or range of movement available to dangerous parts or providing protection during maintenance operations. Examples are:

(a)     providing temporary guards;
(b)     limited movement controls;
(c)     crawl speed operated by hold-to-run controls;
(d)     using a second low-powered visible laser beam to align a powerful invisible one.

222 Other measures to protect against any residual risk include wearing personal protective equipment and provision of instruction and supervision. Although the actual use of these measures falls outside the scope of this regulation, the work equipment should as far as possible be installed to be compatible with their use.

> **Summary of regulation 23**
>
> Where equipment is dangerous or has dangerous parts that project, the equipment should be marked so that employees are not put at risk.

## Regulation 23 Markings

**Regulation     23**

*Every employer shall ensure that work equipment is marked in a clearly visible manner with any marking appropriate for reasons of health and safety.*

**Guidance     23**

223 Some of the markings required by this regulation may also serve as the warning required by regulation 24.

224 There are many circumstances in which marking equipment is appropriate for health or safety reasons. Stop and start controls for equipment need to be identified. The maximum rotation speed of an abrasive wheel should be marked on it. Gas cylinders should indicate (normally by colour) the gas in them. Storage and feed vessels containing hazardous substances should be marked to show their contents, and any hazard associated with them. Pipework for water and compressed air and other mains services should be colour-coded to indicate contents.

225 Some legislation lays down specific circumstances in which markings are needed, and what form they should take. Examples of regulations requiring particular markings are the Ionising Radiations Regulations 1999,[34] and the Dangerous Substances and Explosive Atmospheres Regulations 2002[35] (regulations 6 and 7). Pressure vessels are subject to various regulations, which include requirements for marking the vessel with specific information. Equipment used for lifting loads should be marked with the maximum working load limit (WLL) (rated capacity). Specific information relating to the marking of lifting equipment is set out in regulation 7 of LOLER.

226 You should consider any other marking that might be appropriate for your own purposes, for example numbering machines to aid identification, particularly if the controls or isolators for the machines are not directly attached to them and there could otherwise be confusion.

**Guidance** 23

227 Markings may use words, letters, numbers, or symbols, and the use of colour or shape may be significant. There are nationally or internationally agreed markings relating to some hazards, for example the international symbols for radiation and lasers. Markings should as far as possible conform to such published standards as BS EN ISO 7010[36] or as required by any appropriate legislation such as the Health and Safety (Safety Signs and Signals) Regulations 1996.[37]

> **Short summary of regulation 24**
>
> Regulation 24 makes it clear that warnings are not appropriate unless they are clearly signalling danger.
>
> The regulation focuses on ensuring that warnings are:
> - clear;
> - easy to understand;
> - unmistakeable.

## Regulation 24 Warnings

**Regulation** 24

(1) Every employer shall ensure that work equipment incorporates any warnings or warning devices which are appropriate for reasons of health and safety.

(2) Without prejudice to the generality of paragraph (1), warnings given by warning devices on work equipment shall not be appropriate unless they are unambiguous, easily perceived and easily understood.

**Guidance** 24

228 Warnings or warning devices are appropriate where risks to health or safety remain after hardware measures have been taken. They may be incorporated into systems of work (including permit-to-work systems). A warning is normally in the form of a notice or similar. Examples are positive instructions ('hard hats must be worn'), prohibitions ('not to be operated by people under 18 years'), restrictions ('do not heat above 60 °C'). A warning device is an active unit giving a signal; the signal will typically be visible or audible, and is often connected into equipment so that it is active only when a hazard exists.

229 In some cases, warnings and warning devices will be specified in other legislation, for example automatic safe load indicators on mobile cranes on construction sites, or 'X-rays on' lights.

230 Warnings can be permanent printed ones; these may be attached to or incorporated into the equipment or positioned close to it. There may also be a need for portable warnings to be posted during temporary operations such as maintenance; these may form part of a permit-to-work system.

231 In some cases words can be augmented or replaced by appropriate graphical signs. So as to be readily understood, such signs will normally need to be from a nationally or internationally agreed standard. The Health and Safety (Safety Signs and Signals) Regulations 1996 are relevant here.

232 Warning devices can be:

(a) audible, for example reversing alarms on construction vehicles;
(b) visible, for example a light on a control panel that a fan on a microbiological cabinet has broken down or a blockage has occurred on a particular machine;
(c) an indication of imminent danger, for example machine about to start, or development of a fault condition (ie pump failure or conveyor blockage indicator on a control panel);
(d) the continued presence of a potential hazard (for example, hotplate or laser on).

A particular warning may use both types of device simultaneously, for example, some automatic safe load indicators on mobile cranes.

233 Warnings must be easily perceived and understood, and unambiguous. It is important to consider factors which affect people's perception of such devices, especially for warnings of imminent danger. Visual warnings will be effective only if a person frequently looks in a particular direction, and therefore may not be as widely applicable as audible signals. Appropriate choice of colour and flashing can catch attention, and also reinforce the warning nature of a visual signal. The sound given by an audible signal should be of such a type that people unambiguously perceive it as a warning. This means that it must be possible to distinguish between the warnings given by separate warning devices and between the warnings and any other, unrelated, signals which may be in operation at the time. It may not be possible to rely on audible signals in a noisy environment, nor in circumstances where many such signals are expected to be active at one time.

## Regulations 25–30: Mobile work equipment

234 These regulations implement additional requirements for mobile work equipment, which relate to the equipment when it is travelling. Except for the specific requirements of regulation 30 which deals with drive shafts, they are not intended to apply to moving parts of mobile work equipment which is carrying out work in a static position, for example an excavator involved in digging operations.

235 Where vehicles are designed primarily for travel on public roads, compliance with the Road Vehicles (Construction and Use) Regulations 1986 will normally be enough to comply with regulations 25–30.

## What is mobile work equipment?

236 For the purposes of PUWER regulations 25–30, mobile work equipment is any work equipment which carries out work while it is travelling or which travels between different locations where it is used to carry out work. Such equipment would normally be moved on, for example wheels, tracks, rollers, skids etc. Mobile work equipment may be self-propelled, towed or remote controlled and may incorporate attachments.

## Self-propelled mobile work equipment

237 Self-propelled mobile work equipment is work equipment which is propelled by its own motor or mechanism. The motor or mechanism may be powered by energy generated on the mobile work equipment itself, for example by an internal combustion engine, or through connection to a remote power source, such as an electric cable, electric induction or hydraulic line.

## Attachment

238 Attachments are work equipment which may be mounted on self-propelled mobile work equipment to alter its characteristics. For example, a load rotator fitted to a lift truck will alter its load-handling capabilities and may alter its safety characteristics, such as stability. Attachments are not considered to be mobile work

equipment in their own right but if they can affect the safety of the self-propelled mobile work equipment when they are attached, they are considered to be part of the self-propelled work equipment. Attachments may be non-powered, powered by an independent power source or powered by the self-propelled work equipment to which they are attached.

## Towed mobile work equipment

239  Towed mobile work equipment includes work equipment such as towed machines and trailers which are primarily self-supporting on, for example, their own wheels. They may have moving parts which are:

(a)    powered by the vehicle (for example, a power harrow);
(b)    an integral power source (for example, a powered crop sprayer);
(c)    they may have no moving parts and function as a result of the movement of the mobile work equipment (for example, a plough or trailer).

## Remote-controlled mobile work equipment

240  For the purposes of PUWER, remote-controlled mobile work equipment is operated by controls which are not physically connected to it, for example radio control.

## Pedestrian-controlled work equipment

241  Pedestrian-controlled work equipment, for example, a lawnmower, is not generally covered by regulations 25–30 of PUWER irrespective of whether some functions are powered or not.

# Regulation 25 Employees carried on mobile work equipment

**Regulation 25**

*Every employer shall ensure that no employee is carried by mobile work equipment unless —*

*(a)    it is suitable for carrying persons; and*
*(b)    it incorporates features for reducing to as low as is reasonably practicable risks to their safety, including risks from wheels or tracks.*

**ACOP 25**

**242  You should ensure that risks to the operator and other workers due to the mobile work equipment travelling are controlled. Workers should be protected against falling out of the equipment and from unexpected movement.**

**Guidance 25**

## When regulation 25 applies

243  Regulation 25 contains general requirements which cover the risks to people (drivers, operators and passengers) carried by mobile work equipment when it is travelling. This includes risks associated with people falling from the equipment or from unexpected movement while it is in motion or stopping. It also covers risks

associated with the environment and the place in which the mobile work equipment is used (for example, falling objects, low roofs and the surfaces on which it operates). Regulations 26–30 deal with particular risks.

244 Regulation 25(b) also specifically covers the risks from wheels and tracks when the equipment is travelling but it does not cover the risks from other moving parts, which are covered by regulation 11. In addition, it does not cover the risks associated with mounting or dismounting from the equipment which is covered by the HSW Act.

## Suitable for carrying people

245 Operator stations with seats or work platforms normally provide a secure place on which the drivers and other people can travel on mobile work equipment.

## Seating

246 Seats should be provided wherever necessary. They can provide security for:

(a) drivers who need to be seated when operating mobile work equipment, for example the seat on a site dumper;
(b) people who need to be seated while being transported by the mobile work equipment, for example bench seats in mine locomotive manriding carriages;
(c) people who are involved in on-board work activities which are best carried out in a seated position.

## Cabs, operators' stations and work platforms

247 Cabs, operators' stations and work platforms, with suitable side, front and rear barriers or guard rails can prevent people from falling from mobile work equipment when it is travelling. Where provided, they should be properly designed and constructed.

## Equipment not specifically designed for carrying people

248 Under exceptional circumstances mobile work equipment may be used to carry people although it is not specifically designed for this purpose, for example trailers used to carry farmworkers during harvest time. Under these circumstances the mobile work equipment must have features to prevent people falling from it and to allow them to stabilise themselves while it is travelling, for example trailers with sides of appropriate height or by providing a secure handhold. People would also need to be able to safely mount and dismount.

## Falling object protective structures (FOPS)

249 If people carried on the mobile work equipment are at significant risk of injury from objects falling on them while it is in use, a FOPS should be provided. This could be a suitably strong safety cab or protective cage which provides adequate protection in the working environment in which the mobile equipment is used.

### Restraining systems

250 The need for restraining systems on mobile work equipment is determined by the risks to workers operating and riding on the mobile work equipment and the practicability of fitting and using such restraints. Restraining systems can be full-body seat belts, lap belts or purpose-designed restraining systems. When assessing the need for restraining systems and the nature of seat restraint required, the risk of people being injured through contact with or being flung from the mobile work equipment if it comes to a sudden stop, or moves unexpectedly, should be taken into account. The need for protection against risks for rolling over and overturning (regulations 26–27) should also be taken into account when deciding whether restraining systems should be fitted.

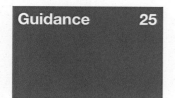

### Speed adjustment

**251 If work needs to be carried out during the journey, speeds should be adjusted as necessary.**

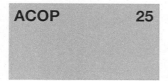

252 When carrying people, mobile work equipment should be driven within safe speed limits to ensure that the equipment is stable when cornering and on all the surfaces and gradients on which it is allowed to travel. In addition, the speeds at which the mobile machinery travels should be limited to avoid sudden movements which could put people being carried at risk. See guidance on motor vehicles in paragraph 21 and on driver training in paragraph 132.

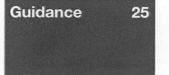

### Guards and barriers

**253 You should ensure that guards and/or barriers fitted to mobile work equipment, which are designed to prevent contact with wheels and tracks, are suitable and effective.**

254 Where there is a foreseeable risk to contact with wheels or tracks when mobile equipment is travelling, adequate separation needs to be provided between people and the wheels and tracks. This can be achieved by positioning cabs, operator stations or work platforms and any suitable barriers, such as robust guard rails or fenders, in positions which prevent the wheels and tracks being reached.

## Regulation 26 Rolling over of mobile work equipment

**Regulation**    **26**

(1) *Every employer shall ensure that where there is a risk to an employee riding on mobile work equipment from its rolling over, it is minimised by—*

(a) *stabilising the work equipment;*
(b) *a structure which ensures that the work equipment does no more than fall on its side;*
(c) *a structure giving sufficient clearance to anyone being carried if it overturns further than that; or*
(d) *a device giving comparable protection.*

(2) *Where there is a risk of anyone being carried by mobile work equipment being crushed by its rolling over, the employer shall ensure that it has a suitable restraining system for him.*

(3) *This regulation shall not apply to a fork-lift truck having a structure described in sub-paragraph (b) or (c) of paragraph (1).*

**Regulation**     **26**

*(4)*    *Compliance with this regulation is not required where—*

*(a)*    *it would increase the overall risk to safety;*

*(b)*    *it would not be reasonably practicable to operate the mobile work equipment in consequence; or*

*(c)*    *in relation to an item of work equipment provided for use in the undertaking or establishment before 5th December 1998 it would not be reasonably practicable.*

**Guidance**     **26**

## When regulation 26 applies

255 In addition to the more general requirements of regulation 25, regulation 26 covers the measures necessary to protect employees carried on mobile work equipment where there are risks from roll-over while it is travelling, for example a moving dumper truck on a construction site or an agricultural tractor forwarding or manoeuvring on a slope. It covers roll-over in which the mobile work equipment may only roll over onto its side or end (ie through 90 degrees) or turn over completely (ie through 180 degrees or more).

256 It does not apply to the risk of mobile work equipment, such as an excavator or a vehicle with a winch, overturning when operating in a stationary position. This is covered by regulation 20.

## Risk assessment

257 To assess the likelihood and potential consequences of roll-over, you will need to take into account the following to determine what safety measures are needed:

(a)    nature of the mobile work equipment and any attachments or accessories fitted to it;

(b)    the effects of any work being carried out on or by the mobile work equipment;

(c)    the conditions in which it is used.

258 When mobile work equipment is travelling, uneven surfaces, variable or slippery ground conditions, excessive gradients, inappropriate speeds, incorrect tyre pressures and sudden changes in direction may lead to roll-over. It can also occur due to the inertia transmitted to the mobile work equipment by attachments used with it, particularly if those attachments are not securely restrained from movement.

259 When mobile work equipment is under power but is restrained from movement, for example when a forestry tractor is being used to drag fallen trees or logs from one place to another and the tree or log snags, you will need to take account of the inherent stability of the mobile work equipment and the forces it can apply.

260 When carrying out a risk assessment it is important to remember that although drivers should be trained to minimise the risk of roll-over, this is not a substitute for hardware measures to prevent roll-over (for example counterbalance weights) or protective structures (for example roll-over protective structures (ROPS) to minimise the risk of injury in the event of a roll-over) where they are necessary.

**Guidance**     26

## Stabilisation

261 Measures that can be taken to stabilise mobile work equipment (ie measures to reduce the risk of roll-over) include fitting appropriate counterbalance weights or increasing its track width by fitting additional or wider wheels. Also, moveable parts which could otherwise create instability by moving around when the mobile work equipment is travelling, may be locked or lashed in stable positions, particularly where locking features are provided for such purposes, for example locking devices for excavator back hoes.

## Structures which prevent rolling over by more than 90 degrees

262 Some types of mobile work equipment will only turn onto their sides if roll-over occurs (ie 90 degree roll-over). For example, the boom of a hydraulic excavator, when positioned in its recommended travelling position, can prevent more than 90 degree roll-over.

## Regulation 26(1)(b)

263 The requirements of regulation 26(1) will be met, if parts of the mobile work equipment prevent it rolling over by more than 90 degrees.

**ACOP**     26

## Roll-over protective structures (ROPS)

**264 You should fit suitable roll-over protective structures to mobile work equipment where necessary to minimise the risks to workers carried, should roll-over occur.**

**Guidance**     26

## Regulation 26(1)(c)

265 ROPS are normally fitted on mobile work equipment which is at risk from 180 degree or more roll-over. They may be structures, frames or cabs which, in the event of roll-over, prevent the work equipment from crushing the people carried by it. ROPS should be capable of withstanding the forces that they would sustain if the mobile work equipment were to roll over through 180 degrees or more.

## Limitations on fitting protective structures

266 A protective structure may not be appropriate where it could increase the overall risk of injury to people operating, driving or riding on mobile work equipment. In these circumstances, where possible, the risks of roll-over should be addressed by other means. An example of where protective structures are not appropriate is when mobile work equipment is required to enter and leave buildings with low roofs and contact could increase the risks to workers.

267 In workplaces such as orchards or a glasshouse, it may not be reasonably practicable to operate mobile work equipment fitted with a ROP.

## Regulation 26(4)(c)

268 Before fitting ROPS to older mobile work equipment, which has no anchorage points provided on it (in use before 5 December 1998), an engineering analysis

**Guidance**    **26**

should be carried out. The analysis should assess whether it is reasonably practicable to fit adequate anchorage points to the equipment and the structural integrity of any anchorage provided. Some mobile work equipment may not be capable of being fitted with protective structures because mounting points of sufficient strength cannot be provided. This will be true of some equipment in use before 5 December 1998. If the risks associated with the use of the equipment are sufficiently high and it is not reasonably practicable to fit mounting points to allow the fitting of a protective structure, you may need to use other equipment which has, or can have, a protective structure fitted to it.

**ACOP**    **26**

### Restraining systems

**269 You should provide restraining systems on mobile work equipment, where appropriate, if they can be fitted to the equipment, to prevent workers carried from being crushed between any part of the work equipment and the ground, should roll-over occur.**

**Guidance**    **26**

### Regulation 26(2)

270 Where the operator is at risk of falling out and being crushed by the mobile work equipment or its protective structure in the event of roll-over, you should provide a restraining system (for example, a seat belt) if it can be fitted. This restraining system may also be necessary under the more general requirements of regulation 25 to protect against other risks.

271 If the operator is in a fully enclosed protective structure and unable to fall out of the mobile work equipment, they will not be at risk of being crushed between the mobile work equipment and the ground. However, if the operator or people carried are likely to be injured through contact with the inside of the structure during roll-over, a restraining system may be necessary.

### Mounting points for restraining systems

272 Any restraining system needs to be fitted to appropriate anchorage points on the mobile work equipment to ensure its integrity and reliability in use. Substantial structural modification should be made on some older types of work equipment in use before 5 December 1998 to allow a restraining system to be fitted. Under these circumstances it is reasonably practicable to fit a restraining system if the risks involved are sufficiently high to justify the necessary modifications. Alternatively you should use other work equipment which has or can have a restraining system fitted to it.

**ACOP**    **26**

### Tractors

**273 If a tractor is fitted with a ROP rather than a cab, a restraining system will be needed.**

**Guidance**    **26**

274 Despite compliance with the Agriculture (Tractor Cabs) Regulations 1974,[38] if the operator or people carried are likely to be injured through contact with the inside of the structure during roll-over, it is likely that you will need to provide a seat restraining system.

# Regulation 27 Overturning of fork-lift trucks

| Regulation | 27 |

*Every employer shall ensure that a fork-lift truck to which regulation 26(3) refers and which carries an employee is adapted or equipped to reduce to as low as is reasonably practicable the risk to safety from its overturning.*

| Guidance | 27 |

## What regulation 27 covers

275  This regulation applies to lift trucks (LTs) fitted with vertical masts, which effectively protect seated operators from being crushed between the LT and the ground in the event of roll-over, and other LTs fitted with a ROPS, for example rough terrain variable reach trucks when they are used with lift attachments. Other types of LT are covered by regulation 26.

## Roll-over protection

276  The mast of a vertical-masted LT will generally prevent an LT overturning by more than 90 degrees, provided it has sufficient strength and dimensions for this purpose. A variable reach truck LT, however, is capable of rolling over 180 degrees or more and would need a ROPS to protect the operator if it is used in circumstances where there is a risk of it rolling over.

| ACOP | 27 |

## Restraining systems

**277  For lift trucks fitted with either a mast or a roll-over protective structure, you should provide restraining systems where appropriate, if such systems can be fitted to the equipment, to prevent workers carried from being crushed between any part of the truck and the ground, should it overturn.**

| Guidance | 27 |

278  If the risk assessment shows that an LT with a seated ride-on operator can roll over in use and there is a risk of the operator leaving the operating position and being crushed between the LT and the ground, a restraining system, such as a seat belt, will be required. Restraining systems are also required on any LT which is fitted with a ROPS, for example a variable reach truck to protect operators from the risks of injury from 180 degrees or more roll-over. To be effective, the restraining system should prevent operators or others carried from falling out or being trapped by the LT or its protective structure in the event of roll-over.

279  There is a history of accidents on counterbalanced, centre control, high lift trucks that have a sit-down operator. Restraining systems will normally be required on these trucks to protect operators from the risks of roll-over.

## Where restraining systems are not required

280  Substantial structural modification may be necessary on some older LTs provided for use before 5 December 1998 to allow seat belts or other types of restraining system to be fitted. Under these circumstances it is reasonably practicable to fit a restraining system if the risks involved are sufficiently high to justify the necessary modifications. Where seat restraints cannot be fitted, and the risks are sufficiently high, you should use another LT which has a restraining system.

# Regulation 28 Self-propelled work equipment

| | |
|---|---|
| **Regulation** | **28** |

*Every employer shall ensure that, where self-propelled work equipment may, while in motion, involve risk to the safety of persons—*

*(a) it has facilities for preventing its being started by an unauthorised person;*

*(b) it has appropriate facilities for minimising the consequences of a collision where there is more than one item of rail-mounted work equipment in motion at the same time;*

*(c) it has a device for braking and stopping;*

*(d) where safety constraints so require, emergency facilities operated by readily accessible controls or automatic systems are available for braking and stopping the work equipment in the event of failure of the main facility;*

*(e) where the driver's direct field of vision is inadequate to ensure safety, there are adequate devices for improving his vision so far as is reasonably practicable;*

*(f) if provided for use at night or in dark places—*

*(i) it is equipped with lighting appropriate to the work to be carried out; and*

*(ii) is otherwise sufficiently safe for such use;*

*(g) if it, or anything carried or towed by it, constitutes a fire hazard and is liable to endanger employees, it carries appropriate fire-fighting equipment, unless such equipment is kept sufficiently close to it.*

| | |
|---|---|
| **Guidance** | **28** |

## Regulation 28(a): Preventing unauthorised start-up

281 Self-propelled work equipment should be prevented from unauthorised start-up. This can be achieved if it has a starter key or device which is issued or made accessible only to authorised people. This means that access to starter keys and starting devices, such as removable dumper starting handles, should be controlled. Vehicles designed primarily for travel on public roads are dealt with in paragraph 235.

## Regulation 28(b): Minimising the consequences of a collision of rail-mounted work equipment

282 If more than one item of rail-mounted work equipment can travel on the same rails at the same time and collision may be foreseen, safety precautions are required to control the risks involved. Where necessary, safe methods of working will need to be followed to reduce the chances of rail-mounted work equipment colliding with each other. Where collision may be foreseen, safety precautions, such as buffers or automatic means of preventing contact, should be provided.

## Regulation 28(c): Devices for stopping and braking

283 All self-propelled mobile work equipment should have brakes to enable it to slow down and stop in a safe distance and park safely. To this end, mobile work equipment should have adequate braking capacity to enable it to be operated safely on the gradients on which it will be used and its parking brakes should be capable of holding it stationary (where appropriate, fully loaded) on the steepest incline that the mobile work equipment may be parked in use.

**Guidance** **28**

284 Other relevant product legislation exists which deals with braking systems on vehicles which may be used on the road as well as at work, such as the Road Vehicles (Construction and Use) Regulations 1986 and Directive 76/432/EEC,[39] as amended by Directive 96/63/EC,[40] dealing with tractor braking. Under normal circumstances, vehicles meeting these requirements would be suitable for use at work.

## Regulation 28(d): Emergency braking and stopping facilities

285 Where there are significant risks associated with failure of the main braking device, a secondary braking system is required. The secondary braking system may operate automatically through spring applied brakes or through a dual circuit system on the service brakes. It may also be operated through the parking brake system or other controls which are easily accessible to the driver. Self-propelled mobile work equipment which will not stop in a safe distance, for example through transmission drag, if service brake failure or faults occur, are normally fitted with secondary braking systems.

## Regulation 28(e): Driver's field of vision

286 This regulation applies when mobile work equipment is about to move or while it is travelling (including manoeuvring). Under these circumstances, where the driver's direct field of vision is inadequate to ensure safety then visibility aids or other suitable devices should be provided so far as is reasonably practicable. Regulation 17 requires that operators of mobile equipment should be able to see anyone who may be put at risk when any control is operated. Therefore, if direct vision is impaired, then mirrors or more sophisticated visual or sensing facilities may be necessary. Regulation 28(e) requires, so far as is reasonably practicable, mobile work equipment to have adequate devices to improve the driver's field of vision where this is otherwise inadequate. Such devices may include mirrors or closed-circuit television (CCTV) and the provision of these devices can be used to meet the requirements of both regulations.

287 Examples of devices which can aid the driver's vision include:

(a) plane, angled and curved mirrors;
(b) Fresnel lenses;
(c) radar;
(d) CCTV systems.

The selection of these devices for use on mobile work equipment is a matter for risk assessment, taking account of the purposes for which the devices are provided and their ability to improve driver visibility.

## Regulation 28(f): Equipping mobile work equipment with lighting for use in the dark

288 In terms of this regulation, 'dark' means any situation where the light levels are not good enough for the driver to operate the self-propelled work equipment safely without risks to themselves or other people in the vicinity.

289 In such situations the equipment needs to be equipped with 'appropriate' lighting. The level of lighting required will depend on the type of equipment being

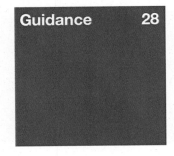

**Guidance** **28**

operated, how it is being operated and the area in which it is operating. Factors you will need to consider are the presence of other people and/or obstacles in the vicinity of the equipment and ground conditions which could lead to risk. In situations where there is a significant risk of an accident, the lighting will need to be at a sufficient level to help control this risk.

290 Regulation 28(f) only covers lighting on mobile work equipment. Lighting provided at the workplace for the use of all work equipment is covered by regulation 21.

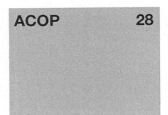

**ACOP** **28**

### Regulation 28(g): The carriage of appropriate fire-fighting appliances

**291 Where escape from self-propelled work equipment in the event of a fire could not be achieved easily, you should ensure that fire-fighting appliances are carried on that equipment.**

**Guidance** **28**

292 This regulation covers the risks to the operators of self-propelled work equipment if the equipment itself or any load handled by it catches fire. If the operators cannot readily escape from the equipment, you should provide appropriate equipment for extinguishing the fire. This will depend on the type of equipment and/or any load it is intended to handle but should include appropriate extinguishers and fire blankets.

293 For self-propelled work equipment that is used on the public highway carrying a dangerous load, it should carry suitable fire extinguishers under the requirements of the Carriage of Dangerous Goods and Use of Transportable Pressure Equipment Regulations 2007.[41]

## Regulation 29 Remote-controlled self-propelled work equipment

**Regulation** **29**

*Every employer shall ensure that where remote-controlled self-propelled work equipment involves a risk to safety while in motion—*

(a) *it stops automatically once it leaves its control range; and*
(b) *where the risk is of crushing or impact it incorporates features to guard against such risk unless other appropriate devices are able to do so.*

**Guidance** **29**

294 For the purposes of regulation 29, 'remote-controlled self-propelled work equipment' is self-propelled work equipment that is operated by controls which have no physical link with it, for example radio control. Pendant-controlled mobile work equipment is not covered by regulation 29.

295 As part of your risk assessment you should consider risks, due to the movement of the equipment, to the person controlling it and to anyone else in the vicinity. You should consider alarms or flashing lights so that other people in the area are aware of its movement, or presence, sensing or contact devices which will protect people from the risks associated with the equipment, ie if people may come close to or contact it.

296 When the equipment is switched off you must ensure that every part of the equipment which could present a risk comes to a safe stop. If the equipment is

controlled manually, the controls for its operation should be of the hold-to-run type so that any hazardous movements can stop when the controls are released.

297 If the equipment leaves its control range, any part of it which could present a risk should be able to stop and remain in a safe state.

## Regulation 30 Drive shafts

*(1) Where the seizure of the drive shaft between mobile work equipment and its accessories or anything towed is likely to involve a risk to safety every employer shall—*

*(a) ensure that the work equipment has a means of preventing such seizure; or*

*(b) where such seizure cannot be avoided, take every possible measure to avoid an adverse effect on the safety of an employee.*

*(2) Every employer shall ensure that—*

*(a) where mobile work equipment has a shaft for the transmission of energy between it and other mobile work equipment; and*

*(b) the shaft could become soiled or damaged by contact with the ground while uncoupled, the work equipment has a system for safeguarding the shaft.*

### Regulation 30(1)

298 A 'drive shaft' is a device which conveys the power from the mobile work equipment to any work equipment connected to it. In agriculture these devices are known as power take-off shafts.

299 'Seizure' refers to stalling of the drive shaft when the operating mechanism of any accessory or anything connected to it becoming incapable of movement due to blockage or some other reason. Under these circumstances regulation 30 applies if the power output of the mobile work equipment is sufficient to cause damage to the connected work equipment which could lead to risk. Regulation 30 does not apply to the risks associated with trapped energy resulting from stalling of the drive shaft if the power output of the mobile work equipment is insufficient to cause damage which could lead to risk. This situation is covered by regulation 19 which deals with the isolation of work equipment from sources of energy.

300 You should assess the risks associated with seizure of the drive shaft. If seizure could lead to risk, for example the ejection of parts, measures should be taken to protect against such risks. For example, slip clutches on the power input connection of the connected work equipment can protect it from damage and guards fitted in accordance with regulation 12 can protect people from ejection risks in the event of equipment break-up.

301 To prevent damage to power take-off shafts in the event of seizure, you should use shafts of adequate length. There should be sufficient overlap between the two halves of the shaft to ensure that it is stable in use, to protect against damage when movements occur in the hitch and to ensure that it has sufficient strength. The shaft needs to be capable of sustaining the full power output of the mobile work equipment, taking account of any slip clutches, shear bolts or similar devices which are provided to limit the torque that the shaft would sustain.

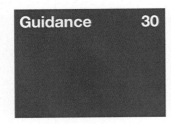

### Regulation 30(2)

302 To prevent damage to the drive shaft and its guard when the equipment is not in use, the drive shaft should be supported on a cradle wherever one is provided. If there is no cradle, it should be supported by other means to give equivalent protection against damage. You should not rest the drive shafts on draw bars, nor drop them on the ground, as this could lead to damage.

Note: Regulations 31-35 and related Schedules 2 and 3 refer to power presses and are not included here. They can be found in *Safe use of power presses*.

## Regulation 36 Exemption for the armed forces

**Regulation  36**

(1)   The Secretary of State for Defence may, in the interests of national security, by a certificate in writing exempt any of the home forces, any visiting force or any headquarters from any requirement or prohibition imposed by these Regulations and any such exemption may be granted subject to conditions and to a limit of time and may be revoked by the said Secretary of State by a certificate in writing at any time.

(2)   In this regulation—

(a)   "the home forces" has the same meaning as in section 12(1) of the Visiting Forces Act 1952;

(b)   "headquarters" has the same meaning as in article 3(2) of the Visiting Forces and International Headquarters (Application of Law) Order 1965;

(c)   "visiting force" has the same meaning as it does for the purposes of any provision of Part I of the Visiting Forces Act 1952.

## Regulation 37 Transitional provision

**Regulation  37**

The requirements in regulations 25 to 30 shall not apply to work equipment provided for use in the undertaking or establishment before 5th December 1998 until 5th December 2002.

# Schedule 1 Instruments which give effect to Community Directives concerning the safety of products

## Regulation 10

| (1) Title | (2) Reference |
| --- | --- |
| The Construction Plant and Equipment (Harmonisation of Noise Emission Standards) Regulations 1985 | S.I. 1985/1968, amended by S.I. 1989/1127 |
| The Construction Plant and Equipment (Harmonisation of Noise Emission Standards) Regulation 1988 | S.I. 1988/361, amended by S.I. 1992/488, 1995/2357 |
| The Electro-medical Equipment (EEC Requirements) Regulations 1988 | S.I. 1988/1586, amended by S.I. 1994/3017 |
| The Low Voltage Electrical Equipment (Safety) Regulations 1989 | S.I. 1989/728, amended by S.I. 1994/3260 |
| The Construction Products Regulations 1991 | S.I. 1991/1620, amended by S.I. 1994/3051 |
| The Simple Pressure Vessels (Safety) Regulations 1991 | S.I. 1991/2749, amended by S.I. 1994/3098 |
| The Lawnmowers (Harmonisation of Noise Emission Standards) Regulations 1992 | S.I. 1992/168 |
| The Gas Appliances (Safety) Regulations 1992 | S.I. 1992/711 |
| The Electromagnetic Compatibility Regulations 1992 | S.I. 1992/2372, amended by S.I. 1994/3080 |
| The Personal Protective Equipment (EC Directive) Regulations 1992 | S.I. 1992/3139, amended by S.I. 1993/3074, 1994/2326, 1996/3039 |
| The Active Implantable Medical Devices Regulations 1992 | S.I. 1992/3146, amended by S.I. 1995/1671 |
| The Medical Devices Regulations 1994 | S.I. 1994/3017 |
| The Electrical Equipment (Safety) Regulations 1994 | S.I. 1994/3260 |
| The Gas Appliances (Safety) Regulations 1995 | S.I. 1995/1629 |
| The Equipment and Protective Systems Intended for Use in Potentially Explosive Atmospheres Regulations 1996 | S.I. 1996/192, amended by S.I. 1998/81, 2001/3766, 2005/830 |
| The Lifts Regulations 1997 | S.I. 1997/831, amended by S.I. 2005/831 |
| The Pressure Equipment Regulations 1999 | S.I. 1999/2001 |
| The Noise Emission in the Environment by Equipment for use Outdoors Regulations 2001 | S.I. 2001/1701 |
| The Cableway Installations Regulations 2004 | S.I. 2004/129 |
| The Supply of Machinery (Safety) Regulations 2008 | S.I. 2008/1597 |

# Appendix 1 Further guidance on regulation 11 – Dangerous parts of machinery

## Explanation of safeguarding terms, regulation 11(2)

1    Guards are physical barriers which prevent access to the danger zone. Fixed guards in regulation 11(2)(b) have no moving parts and are fastened in a constant position relative to the danger zone (see Figure 1). They are kept in place either permanently, by welding for example, or by means of fasteners (screws, nuts etc) making removal/opening impossible without using tools. If by themselves, or in conjunction with the structure of the equipment, they enclose the dangerous parts, fixed guards meet the requirements of the first level of the hierarchy. Note that fixed enclosing guards, and other types of guard, can have openings provided that they comply with appropriate safe reach distances (see BS EN ISO 13857).[42]

2    Other guards in regulation 11(2)(b) include movable guards which can be opened without the use of tools, and fixed guards that are not fully enclosing. These allow limited access through openings, gates etc for feeding materials, making adjustments, cleaning etc (see Figure 2). Movable guards may be power-operated, self-closing, adjustable etc and are likely to require an interlocking device so that:

(a)    the hazardous machine functions covered by the guard cannot operate until the guard is closed;
(b)    if the guard is opened while hazardous machine functions are operating, a stop instruction is given;
(c)    when the guard is closed, the hazardous machine functions covered by the guard can operate, but the closure of the guard does not by itself initiate their operation.

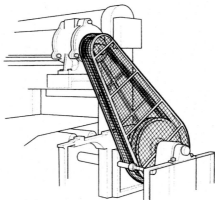

**Figure 1** Fixed enclosing guard

Interlocking guards may be fitted with a locking device so the guard stays closed and locked until any risk of injury from the hazardous machine functions has passed. A control guard (interlocking guard with a start function) is a particular type of interlocking guard which should be used only in certain situations where frequent access is required. It should also fulfil specific conditions, in particular, where there is no possibility of an operator or part of their body remaining in the danger zone or between the danger zone and the guard while the guard is closed (see BS EN 953).[43]

3    Protection devices do not prevent access to the danger zone but stop the movement of the dangerous part before contact is made. They will normally be used in conjunction with a guard. Typical examples are mechanical trip devices, active opto-electronic devices such as light curtains (see Figure 3), pressure-sensitive mats and two-hand controls.

4    Protection appliances are used to hold or manipulate in a way which allows operators to control and feed a loose workpiece at a machine while keeping their body clear of the danger zone. They are commonly used in conjunction with manually fed woodworking machines (see Figure 4) and some other machines such as bandsaws for cutting meat where it is not possible to fully guard the cutting tool. These appliances will normally be used as well as guards.

5    Adequate information, instruction, supervision and training are always important, even if the hazard is protected by hardware measures, however, they are especially important when the risk cannot be adequately eliminated by the hardware measures in regulation 11(2)(a)–(c). It may be necessary to lay down procedures to define what information, instruction, training and supervision must be given, and to restrict use of the equipment to those who have received such instructions etc.

## Selection of measures

6    The guidance outlines how the hierarchy in regulation 11(2) should be applied in selecting safeguarding measures. Within each level of the hierarchy, there may be some choice available. In particular, the second level in the hierarchy allows a choice from among a number of different types of guard or protection device.

7    Regulation 11(2)(b) requires that when it is not practicable to use fixed enclosing guards, either at all or to the extent required for adequate protection, other guards and/or protection devices shall be used as far as practicable. Where, for example, frequent access is required, it may be necessary to choose between an interlocking movable guard or a protection device. The foreseeable probability and severity of injury will influence the choice of measures from among the range of guards and protection devices available. Regulation 11(3)(a) requires that these must be suitable for their purpose. It is likely that some fixed guarding will be required to ensure that access can only be made through the movable opening guard or protection device. The use of movable guards which are interlocked is well established. Protection devices need to be carefully applied, taking into account the particular circumstances and consequences of their failing to act as required.

8    Fixed distance guards, adjustable guards and other guards which do not completely enclose the dangerous parts should only be used in situations where it is not practicable to use fixed enclosing guards or protection devices which would give a greater level of protection.

## Features of guards and protection devices, regulation 11(3)

### Regulation 11(3)(a)
9    All guards and protection devices provided must be suitable for their purpose. In deciding what is suitable, employers should first establish the foreseeable risks from the machine and then follow guidance contained in national and international standards guidance from HSE and industry associations, normal industrial practice and their own knowledge of the particular circumstances in which the machine is to be used. You can find further information on the HSE website www.hse.gov.uk./work-equipment-machinery.

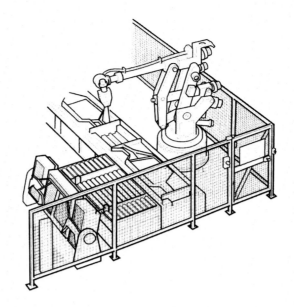

**Figure 2** Perimeter fence guard with fixed panels and interlocking access door

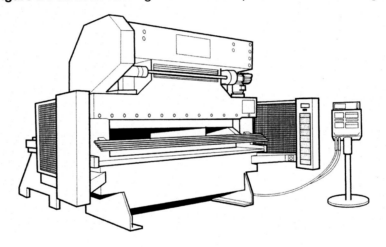

**Figure 3** Photoelectric device fitted to a press brake

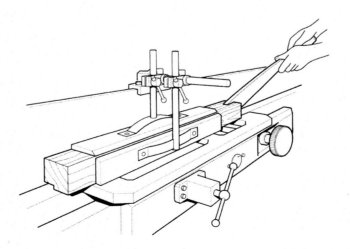

**Figure 4** A push stick in use at a woodworking machine

10    A protection device or interlocking system should be designed so that it will only operate as intended. Furthermore, if a component deteriorates or fails, the device or system should as far as possible fail in a safe manner by inhibiting the dangerous action of the machine. The force of this requirement depends on the combination of probability of failure and severity of the injury, should the system fail. If the overall risk is high, there should be adequate provision to counteract the effects of failure. Guidance on appropriate levels of protection is given in the publications referred to in paragraph 9 of this Appendix.

### Regulation 11(3)(b)

11    Guards and protection devices must be of good construction, sound material and adequate strength. They must be capable of doing the job they are intended to do. Several factors can be considered:

(a)    construction material (metal, plastic, laminated glass etc);
(b)    form of the material (sheet, open mesh, bars etc);
(c)    method of fixing.

12    Good construction involves design and layout as well as the mechanical nature and quality of the construction. Foreseeable use and misuse should be taken into account.

### Regulation 11(3)(c)

13    Guards and protection devices must be maintained in an efficient state, in efficient working order and in good repair. This is an important requirement as many accidents have occurred when guards have not been maintained. It is a particular example of the general requirement under regulation 5 to maintain equipment. Compliance can be achieved by the use of an effective check procedure for guards and protection devices, together with any necessary follow-up action. In the case of protection devices or interlocks, some form of functional check or test is desirable.

14    For inspection and thorough examination of power presses and their guards and protection devices, see *Safe use of power presses*.

### Regulation 11(3)(d)

15    Guards and protection devices must not themselves lead to any increased risk to health or safety. One effect of this sub-paragraph is to prevent use of inherently hazardous measures for guarding.

16    A second effect is that guards must be constructed so that they are not themselves dangerous parts. If a guard is power operated or assisted, the closing or opening action might create a potentially dangerous trap which needs secondary protection, for example a leading-edge trip bar or pressure-sensitive strip.

17    The main concern is the overall effect on risk. The fact that a guard may itself present a minor risk should not rule out its use if it can protect against the risk of major injury. For example, sweep-away guards or manually-actuated sliding access gates might be able to cause minor injury, but their use in guarding against more serious risks is justified.

### Regulation 11(3)(e)

18    Guards and protection devices must be designed and installed so that they cannot be easily bypassed or disabled. This refers to accidental or deliberate action that removes the protection offered. By regulation 11(3)(a), guards must be suitable for their purpose, and one consequence of this is that simple mechanical bypassing or disabling should not be possible.

19    Movable panels in guards giving access to dangerous parts or movable guards themselves will often need to be fitted with an interlocking device. This device must be designed and installed so that it is difficult or impossible to bypass or defeat. Guidance on the selection and design of interlocking devices is available from BS 14119 and the sources listed in paragraph 9 of this Appendix.

20    In some cases, bypassing is needed for a particular purpose such as maintenance. The risks in such circumstances must be carefully assessed. As far as possible, the risks should be reduced or eliminated by appropriate design of the machinery (see regulation 22).

### Regulation 11(3)(f)

21    Guards and protection devices must be situated at a sufficient distance from the danger zone they are protecting. In the case of solid fixed enclosing guards, there is no minimum distance between guard and danger zone, except that required for good engineering design. However, the gap between a fence-type guard or protection device and machine should normally be sufficiently small to prevent anybody remaining in it without being detected; alternatively, the space between guard or protection device and machine should be monitored by a suitable presence-sensing device.

22    Where guarding is provided with holes or gaps (for visibility, ventilation or weight reduction, for example), or is not fully enclosing, the holes must be positioned or sized so that it prevents foreseeable access to the danger zone. Published national and international standards (for example, BS EN ISO 13857) give guidance on suitable distances and opening sizes in different circumstances.

23    The positioning of protection devices which enable hazardous machine operation to stop before access can be gained to its danger zone will be affected by both the characteristics of the device itself (response time) and those of the machine to which it is fitted (time needed to stop). In these circumstances the device must be positioned so that it meets published criteria for the performance of such a system. Refer to the relevant standard (BS EN 13855)[45] and guidance (HSG180).[46]

24    Safeguarding is normally attached to the machine, but the regulation does preclude the use of free-standing guards or protection devices. In such cases, the guards or protection devices must be fixed in an appropriate position relative to the machine.

### Regulation 11(3)(g)

25    Guards and protection devices must not unduly restrict the view of the operating cycle of the machinery, where such a view is necessary. You don't usually need to be able to see all the machine; the part that needs to be seen is normally that which is acting directly on material or a workpiece.

26    Operations for which there should be a view include those where the operator controls and feeds a loose workpiece at a machine. Examples include manually fed woodworking machines and food slicers. Many of these operations involve the use of protection appliances.

27    If the machine process should be seen, but cannot be, there is a temptation for the operator to remove or disable guards or interlocks. In such cases, there should be some view of the work. Examples are a hopper feeding a screw conveyor, milling machines, and power presses.

28   In other cases it may be convenient but not absolutely necessary to see the entire operating cycle. The regulation does not prohibit providing a view in these cases, but does not require it; an example is an industrial tumble drier.

29   Where an operation protected by guards needs to be seen, the guard should be provided with viewing slits or properly constructed panels, perhaps backed up by internal lighting, enabling the operator to see the operation. The arrangements to ensure visibility should not prevent the guarding from carrying out its proper function; but any restriction of view should be the minimum compatible with that. An example of a guard providing necessary vision is viewing slits provided in the top guard of a circular saw.

### Regulation 11(3)(h)
30   Guards and protection devices must be constructed or adapted so that they allow operations necessary to fit or replace parts and for maintenance work, restricting access so that it is allowed only to the area where the work is to be carried out and, if possible, without having to dismantle the guard or protection device.

31   This regulation applies to the design of guards or protection devices so as to reduce risks arising from some particular operations. Regulation 22 applies to the design of equipment as a whole so that maintenance and similar operations can be carried out safely; regulation 11 is restricted to machine safeguards.

32   The aim is to design the safeguards so that operations like fitting or changing parts or maintenance can be done with minimal risk. If risk assessment shows this is not already the case, it may be possible to adapt the safeguarding appropriately.

33   Ideally, the machine is designed so that operations can be done in an area without risk, for example by using remote adjustment or maintenance points. If the work has to be done in the enclosed or protected area, the safeguarding should be designed to restrict access just to that part where the work is to be carried out. This may mean using a series of guards.

34   If possible, the guard or protection device should not have to be dismantled. This is because of the possibility that after reassembly, the guard or device may not work to its original performance standard.

### Regulation 11(4)
35   Protection appliances should be suitable for their application. Factors for consideration come under the same headings as those for guards and protection devices as in regulation 11(3). Many of these are common sense matters. Their design, material, manufacturer and maintenance should all be adequate for the job they do. They should allow the person to use them without having to get too close to the danger zone, and they should not block the view of the workpiece.

# Appendix 2 Approved Code of Practice added by AUWED in 1998 and made under Section 2 HSWA

# The Health and Safety at Work etc Act 1974, Section 2

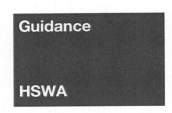

## Introduction

1    The Use of Work Equipment Amending Directive (AUWED) introduced some requirements for the management of work equipment. These requirements are fulfilled through Section 2 of and ACOP to support it which is reproduced in the following paragraphs.

*(1)    It shall be the duty of every employer to ensure, so far as is reasonably practicable, the health, safety and welfare at work of all his employees.*

*(2)    Without prejudice to the generality of an employer's duty under the preceding subsection, the matters to which that duty extends include in particular—*

*(a)    the provision and maintenance of plant and systems of work that are, so far as is reasonably practicable, safe and without risks to health;*

*(b)    arrangements for ensuring, so far as is reasonably practicable, safety and absence of risks to health in connection with the use, handling, storage and transport of articles and substances;*

*(c)    the provision of such information, instruction, training and supervision as is necessary to ensure, so far as is reasonably practicable, the health and safety at work of his employees;*

*(d)    so far as is reasonably practicable as regards any place of work under the employer's control, the maintenance of it in a condition that is safe and without risks to health and the provision and maintenance of means of access and egress from it that are safe and without such risks;*

*(e)    the provision and maintenance of a working environment for his employees that is, so far as is reasonably practicable, safe, without risks to health, and adequate as regards facilities and arrangements for their welfare at work.*

## Erecting or dismantling work equipment

**2    You should ensure that work equipment is erected or dismantled in a safe way, in particular observing any manufacturers' or suppliers' instructions where they exist.**

3    The assembly and dismantling of some items of work equipment, for example airbridges at airports, may be subject to the requirements of CDM.

4    Work equipment should be erected, assembled or dismantled safely and without risk to health. Safe systems of work and safe working practice should be followed to achieve this. A safe system of work is a formal procedure which should

**Guidance**

be followed to ensure that work is carried out safely and is necessary where risks cannot be adequately controlled by other means.

5    The work should be planned and hazards identified. You should ensure that the systems of work to be followed are properly implemented and monitored and that details have been communicated to those at risk.

6    Detailed information about safe systems of work can be found at www.hse.gov.uk/managing.

## Risks from self-propelled work equipment

### *Assessing risks from self-propelled work equipment*
7    The Management Regulations require you to carry out a risk assessment. This risk assessment will identify the hazards, help you evaluate the risks and also decide how to control the risks. Appropriate preventive and protective measures should be taken in the light of the risks identified. The risks which the use of mobile work equipment can create where pedestrians are present include the danger of people being struck, crushed or run over by self-propelled work equipment or being struck by an object falling from a vehicle.

### *Dealing with the risks from self-propelled mobile equipment*
8    In order to control the risks (identified in paragraph 7) which the use of self-propelled work equipment can create for pedestrians, you should consider the following:

(a)    separation of pedestrians and self-propelled mobile work equipment;
(b)    traffic rules;
(c)    traffic signs;
(d)    planning traffic routes;
(e)    traffic speed.

9    Regulation 17 of the Workplace Regulations and its supporting ACOP also deal with the organisation etc of traffic routes and the organisation of workplaces so that pedestrians and vehicles can circulate in a safe manner. This requirement should be considered together with the Workplace ACOP to achieve compliance with both PUWER and the Workplace Regulations.

**HSWA**

**ACOP**

**HSWA**

### *Risks to pedestrians*
**10    You should take measures, where appropriate, to prevent pedestrians coming within the area of operation of self-propelled work equipment. Where this is not reasonably practicable, appropriate measures should be taken to reduce the risks involved, including the operation of appropriate traffic rules.**

**Guidance**

11    Where possible you should keep pedestrians away from self-propelled work equipment. Where this is not possible you are required, so far as is reasonably practicable, to provide and maintain a safe system of work.

### *Traffic rules*
12    Appropriate traffic rules should limit the risks to pedestrians and operators when mobile work equipment is in use, for example, lift trucks operating in a loading bay where there are pedestrians and other vehicles. Traffic rules should be established as part of a safe system of work following risk assessment.

### *Further guidance*
13    More detailed information on workplace transport safety can be found at www.hse.gov.uk/workplacetransport.

**HSWA**

**ACOP**

**HSWA**

**Guidance**

*Lightning*

**14    You should ensure that, where there is a risk to workers arising from lightning strikes to work equipment when it is being used, appropriate safety precautions are followed.**

*Assessing the risks from lightning*

15    Where work equipment may be struck by lightning while being used it should be protected as appropriate from the effects of the lightning. When assessing whether lightning protection is required for work equipment, you should consider whether:

(a)    the area is one in which lightning generally occurs;
(b)    the work equipment is tall or isolated;
(c)    the work equipment contains flammable or explosive substances;
(d)    large numbers of people will be affected by a lightning strike.

16    Types of work equipment which you should consider include:

(a)    cranes being used in isolated areas;
(b)    fairground equipment operating in similar conditions or in the open where large numbers of people are likely to be affected by a lightning strike;
(c)    employees engaged in field work – surveyors etc, where there is a possible risk of lightning strike if the surveying staff/prism is used during a lightning strike.

*Lightning protection*

17    Protection from lightning can be provided by conductors or insulation. There are circumstances where the best way of reducing the risk is to stop working during a lightning storm. For example, a golf professional should avoid playing or teaching during a storm as a metal golf club is an excellent conductor of lightning and golf is often played in open areas or near trees where lightning strikes are likely to occur. Likewise, a surveying team may need to stop work during a storm as would certain utility workers.

*Other information about lightning and lightning protection*

18    Detailed information about lightning, risk assessment, the likelihood of lightning strike and suitable protection is contained in BS EN 62303 Parts 1–4,[47] the British Standard Code of Practice for protection of structures against lightning.

**HSWA**

# Appendix 3 Notice of Approval

By virtue of section 16(4) of the Health and Safety at Work etc Act 1974, and with the consent of the Secretary of State for Work and Pensions, the Health and Safety Executive has on 13 August 2014 approved the revised Code of Practice entitled *Safe use of work equipment* (Fourth edition, 2014, L22).

The revised Code of Practice gives practical guidance with respect to section 2 of the Health and Safety at Work etc Act 1974, the requirements of the Provision and Use of Work Equipment Regulations 1998 and the Management of Health and Safety at Work Regulations 1999. The Code of Practice comes into effect on 28 November 2014.

This revised edition replaces the previous edition entitled *Safe use of work equipment* (Third edition) which came into effect on 5 December 1998.

Signed

TERESA QUINN
Secretary to the Board of the Health and Safety Executive

27 November 2014

# References

1    *Health and Safety at Work etc Act 1974 (c 37)* The Stationery Office 1974 ISBN 978 0 10 543774 1

2    *Safe use of lifting equipment. Lifting Operations and Lifting Equipment Regulations 1998. Approved Code of Practice and guidance* L113 HSE Books 1998 ISBN 978 0 7176 1628 2 www.hse.gov.uk/pubns/books/l113.htm

3    *Workplace health, safety and welfare. Workplace (Health, Safety and Welfare) Regulations 1992. Approved Code of Practice and guidance* L24 (Second edition) HSE Books 2013 ISBN 978 0 7176 6583 9 www.hse.gov.uk/pubns/books/l24.htm

4    *Work with display screen equipment: Health and Safety (Display Screen Equipment) Regulations 1992 as amended by the Health and Safety (Miscellaneous Amendments) Regulations 2002. Guidance on Regulations* L26 (Second edition) HSE Books 2003 ISBN 978 0 7176 2582 6 www.hse.gov.uk/pubns/books/l26.htm

5    *Personal Protective Equipment at Work (Second edition). Personal Protective Equipment at Work Regulations 1992 (as amended). Guidance on Regulations* L25 (Second edition) HSE Books 2005 ISBN 978 0 7176 6139 8 www.hse.gov.uk/pubns/books/l25.htm

6    *Managing health and safety in construction. Construction (Design and Management) Regulations 2007. Approved Code of Practice* L144 HSE Books 2007 ISBN 978 0 7176 6223 4 www.hse.gov.uk/pubns/books/l144.htm

7    *The Road Vehicles (Construction and Use) Regulations 1986* SI 1986/1078 The Stationery Office

8    *Working at height: A brief guide* Leaflet INDG401(rev2) HSE Books 2014 www.hse.gov.uk/pubns/indg401.htm

9    *The Management of Health and Safety at Work Regulations 1999* SI 1999/3242 The Stationery Office

10   *Safe use of power presses. Provision and Use of Work Equipment Regulations 1998 (as applied to power presses). Approved Code of Practice and guidance* L112 (Second edition) HSE Books 2014 ISBN 978 0 7176 6620 1 www.hse.gov.uk/pubns/books/l112.htm

11   *Safe use of woodworking machinery. Provision and Use of Work Equipment Regulations 1998 as applied to woodworking machinery. Approved Code of Practice and guidance* L114 (Second edition) HSE Books 2014 ISBN 978 0 7176 6621 8 www.hse.gov.uk/pubns/books/l114.htm

12   *The Air Navigation Order 2009* SI 2009/3015 The Stationery Office

13    *Consulting employees on health and safety: A brief guide to the law* Leaflet INDG232(rev2) HSE Books 2013 www.hse.gov.uk/pubns/indg232.htm

14    *The Health and Safety at Work etc. Act 1974 (Application outside Great Britain) Order 2013* SI 2013/240 The Stationery Office

15    *The Merchant Shipping and Fishing Vessels (Provision and Use of Work Equipment) Regulations 2006* SI 2006/2183 The Stationery Office

16    *Merchant Shipping Act 1995* SI 1995/21 The Stationery Office

17    *The Offshore Installations (Safety Case) Regulations 2005* SI 2005/3117 The Stationery Office

18    *The Offshore Installations and Pipeline Works (Management and Administration) Regulations 1995* SI 1995/738 The Stationery Office

19    *Risk assessment: A brief guide to controlling risks in the workplace* Leaflet INDG163(rev4) HSE Books 2014 www.hse.gov.uk/pubns/indg163.htm

20    *Confined spaces: A brief guide to working safely* Leaflet INDG258(rev1) HSE Books 2013 www.hse.gov.uk/pubns/indg258.htm

21    *Control of substances hazardous to health (COSHH). The Control of Substances Hazardous to Health Regulations 2002 (as amended). Approved Code of Practice and guidance* L5 (Sixth edition) HSE Books 2013 ISBN 978 0 7176 6582 2 www.hse.gov.uk/pubns/books/l5.htm

22    *Reporting accidents and incidents at work: A brief guide to the Reporting of Injuries, Diseases and Dangerous Occurrences Regulations 2013 (RIDDOR)* Leaflet INDG453(rev1) HSE Books 2013 www.hse.gov.uk/pubns/indg453.htm

23    *Safety of pressure systems: Pressure Systems Safety Regulations 2000. Approved Code of Practice* L122 HSE Books 2000 ISBN 978 0 7176 1767 8 www.hse.gov.uk/pubns/books/l122.htm

24    *Control of lead at work. Control of Lead at Work Regulations 2002. Approved Code of Practice and guidance* L132 (Third edition) HSE Books 2002 ISBN 978 0 7176 2565 9 www.hse.gov.uk/pubns/books/l132.htm

25    *Managing and working with asbestos: Control of Asbestos Regulations 2012. Approved Code of Practice and guidance* L143 (Second edition) HSE Books 2013 ISBN 978 0 7176 6618 8 www.hse.gov.uk/pubns/books/l143.htm

26    *The Mines (Shafts and Winding) Regulations 1993* SI 1993/302 The Stationery Office

27    *Safety in the use of abrasive wheels* HSG17 (Third edition) HSE Books 2000 ISBN 978 0 7176 1739 5 www.hse.gov.uk/pubns/books/hsg17.htm

28    *Buying new machinery: A short guide to the law and your responsibilities when buying new machinery for use at work* Leaflet INDG271(rev1) HSE Books 2011 www.hse.gov.uk/pubns/indg271.htm

29    BS EN 60204-1 *Safety of machinery. Electrical equipment of machines. General requirements* British Standards Institution

30    BS 3641-2:1980 *Systems for machine tools. Specification for numerical control symbols* British Standards Institution BS 3641-3:1973 *Specification for symbols for machine tools. Additional general symbols* British Standards Institution

31    BS EN 13849-1 *Safety of machinery. Safety-related parts of control systems. General principles for design* British Standards Institution

32    BS EN 62061:2005+A1:2013 *Safety of machinery. Functional safety of safety-related electrical, electronic and programmable electronic control systems* British Standards Institution

33    *Memorandum of guidance on the Electricity at Work Regulations 1989.* Guidance on Regulations HSR25 (Second edition) HSE Books 2007 ISBN 978 0 7176 6228 9 www.hse.gov.uk/pubns/hsr25.htm

34    *Work with ionising radiation: Ionising Radiations Regulations 1999: Approved Code of Practice and guidance* L121 HSE Books 2000 ISBN 978 0 7176 1746 3 www.hse.gov.uk/pubns/books/l121.htm

35    *Dangerous substances and explosive atmospheres: Dangerous Substances and Explosive Atmospheres Regulations 2002. Approved Code of Practice and guidance* L138 (Second edition) HSE Books 2013 ISBN 978 0 7176 6616 4 www.hse.gov.uk/pubns/books/l138.htm

36    BS EN ISO 7010 *Graphical symbols: Safety colours and safety signs. Registered safety signs* British Standards Institution

37    *Safety signs and signals. The Health and Safety (Safety Signs and Signals) Regulations 1996. Guidance on Regulations* L64 (Second edition) HSE Books 2009 ISBN 978 0 7176 6359 0 www.hse.gov.uk/pubns/books/l64.htm

38    *The Agriculture (Tractor Cabs) Regulations 1974* SI 1974/2034 The Stationery Office

39    Directive 76/432/EEC *Wheeled agricultural or forestry tractors: Braking devices*

40    *Commission Directive 96/63/EC amending Council Directive 76/432/EEC on the approximation of the laws of the Member States relating to the braking devices of wheeled agricultural or forestry tractors*

41    *The Carriage of Dangerous Goods and Use of Transportable Pressure Equipment Regulations 2007* SI 2007/1573 British Standards Institution

42    BS EN ISO 13857 *Safety of machinery. Safety distances to prevent hazard zones being reached by upper and lower limbs* British Standards Institution

43    BS EN 953:1997+A1:2009 *Safety of machinery. Guards. General requirements for the design and construction of fixed and movable guards* British Standards Institution

44    BS EN ISO 14119:2013 *Safety of machinery. Interlocking devices associated with guards. Principle for design and selection* British Standards Institution

45    BS EN 13855 *Safety of machinery. Positioning of safeguards with respect to the approach speeds of parts of the human body* British Standards Institution

46    *Application of electro-sensitive protective equipment using light curtains and light beam devices to machinery* HSG180 HSE Books 1999 ISBN 978 0 7176 1550 6 www.hse.gov.uk/pubns/books/hsg180.htm

47    BS EN 62303 *Protection against lightning Parts 1–4* British Standards Institution

# Further reading

*EH40/2005 Workplace exposure limits: Containing the list of workplace exposure limits for use with the Control of Substances Hazardous to Health Regulations (as amended)* Environmental Hygiene Guidance Note EH40 (Second edition) HSE Books 2011 ISBN 978 0 7176 6446 7 www.hse.gov.uk/pubns/books/eh40.htm

*The Electrical Equipment (Safety) Regulations 1994* SI 1994/3260 The Stationery Office

*Rider-operated lift trucks: Operator training and safe use. Approved Code of Practice and guidance* L117 (Third edition) HSE Books 2013 ISBN 978 0 7176 6441 2 www.hse.gov.uk/pubns/books/l117.htm

*The Supply of Machinery (Safety) (Amendment) Regulations 2011* SI 2011/2157 The Stationery Office

*The Supply of Machinery (Safety) Regulations 2008* SI 2008/1597 The Stationery Office

*Workplace transport safety: An employers' guide* HSG136 HSE Books 2014 ISBN 978 0 7176 6636 2 www.hse.gov.uk/pubns/books/hsg136.htm

# Further information

For information about health and safety, or to report inconsistencies or inaccuracies in this guidance, visit www.hse.gov.uk. You can view HSE guidance online and order priced publications from the website. HSE priced publications are also available from bookshops.

British Standards can be obtained in PDF or hard copy formats from BSI: http://shop.bsigroup.com or by contacting BSI Customer Services for hard copies only Tel: 0845 086 9001 email: cservices@bsigroup.com.

The Stationery Office publications are available from The Stationery Office, PO Box 29, Norwich NR3 1GN Tel: 0870 600 5522 Fax: 0870 600 5533 email: customer.services@tso.co.uk Website: www.tsoshop.co.uk. (They are also available from bookshops.) Statutory Instruments can be viewed free of charge at www.legislation.gov.uk where you can also search for changes to legislation.

Printed and published by the Health and Safety Executive 11/14